WOOLWICH [463777] [14-6-61]

Panorama looking east over Bostall Woods. The River Thames and Plumstead Marshes can just be made out in the upper-left corner of the photograph.

CHISLEHURST [466705] [23-5-72]

Panorama looking west-south-west towards Bromley, with the edge of Petts Wood just visible on the left of the picture. Despite recent encroachments by London, Chislehurst remains a relatively small 'greenbelt' town.

ORPINGTON [475662] [23-5-72]

A view of several of the large housing estates that have all but engulfed this London suburb. From the air a general feeling of spaciousness is obtained that is not always apparent on the ground.

ERITH [490771] [18-6-80]

Panorama looking north across the River Thames. Keen observers will notice the Thames sailing barge on the river, to the right of the picture.

DARTFORD   [552738] [2-8-66]

Panorama looking north-west towards Erith. The River Thames is to the top-right of the picture. The River Darent can be seen snaking its way diagonally across the photograph from the Thames to the large white building in the centre, overlooked by the railway station.

SWANSCOMBE [593738] [7-7-54]

Looking north-east across one of the many chalk pits in the area, created for the manufacture of cement. Since this photograph was taken the main chalk pit has been worked out and is soon to be landscaped and developed as an amenity feature.

NORTHFLEET [614755] [21-7-59]

Panorama looking south-east over the heavily industrialised banks of the Thames. Little has changed here, except the infilling of some of the open spaces towards Singlewell, at the top of the picture.

GRAVESEND   [646740] [13-6-60]

Looking north-east across the Thames, showing the impressive outline of Tilbury Fort across the river, top-left. The railway station can be seen just up from the centre of the picture, near where the two main roads converge to form a 'V' shape.

MEOPHAM [645660] [4-6-65]

Panorama looking north, with Gravesend and the River Thames just visible running across the top of the picture. The church can be seen towards the bottom of the photograph, with Meopham Court just to the right. The parkland to the left-centre is Camer Country Park.

LEEDS CASTLE [836533] [24-7-48]

Little has changed since this view of Leeds Castle was taken, except that a golf course now occupies the far bank of the lake. From the air the castle looks even more enchanting than from the ground.

WEST MALLING [683577] [7-7-54]

Another early view showing West Malling Abbey, just above centre. It is now occupied by Anglican Benedictine nuns and Anglican Cistercians. The main village lies to the west, but the rich variety of architecture is clearly displayed here.

BOROUGH GREEN   [590571] [23-5-72]

Panorama looking north-east over Borough Green (right-centre) and Wrotham (left-centre) prior to the construction of the M26 and M20 motorways. Wrotham has since been relegated to a position occupying a virtual island site between these two motorways.

MEREWORTH   [668533] [18-6-52]

Mereworth Castle is really a Palladian mansion, unique in Kent. It was built in 1723 on the site of the original village, which was moved half-a-mile further west. This rare view shows the perfect symmetry of its design and its picturesque grounds, which are seldom seen for the house is not normally open to the public.

SISSINGHURST   [807384] [23-5-72]

The delightful gardens of Sissinghurst Castle (c.1535), laid out by Vita Sackville-West, are one of the National Trust's top attractions, drawing many thousands of visitors each year.

SCOTNEY CASTLE   [689353] [19-7-49]

Another National Trust property, the gardens at Scotney Castle, (14th century) near Lamberhurst, are amongst the loveliest and most romantic in the country.

TUNBRIDGE WELLS   [585395] [18-6-52]

A great deal has changed in Tunbridge Wells in the 30 years since this photograph was taken. Mount Ephraim is situated at the extreme left-centre of the picture with the Common just above. Grosvenor Road runs from near the bottom-left to the centre, where it converges with Mount Pleasant Road, with the High Street beyond and the Pantiles just above.

PENSHURST [527440] [26-6-49]

Looking south over the magnificent Penshurst Place (which dates from 1340) to Penshurst village, with the church in the centre of the photograph. The group of Tudor cottages just beyond the church form the original Leicester Square.

TONBRIDGE [588462] [18-6-52]

The River Medway winds its way through the ancient town centre of Tonbridge, with the remains of the castle just right-of-centre. The extensive railway works can be seen towards the top-left corner.

HADLOW [634498] [18-6-52]

Another early view showing Hadlow shortly after the bulk of Hadlow Castle had been demolished (1951). The remains of this Victorian mansion can be seen near the church at the centre of the photograph. The Maidstone to Tonbridge road cuts across the top-left corner.

EDENBRIDGE   [443462] [14-6-61]

Looking north-north-west towards Crockham Hill, which lies just beyond the top-right corner of the photograph. The church can be seen near the centre, with the railway station above it and to the right.

CROCKHAM HILL   [444514] [7-7-54]

Looking north-west over Crockham Hill Common. Westerham lies to the top-right of the picture, with Bromley faintly discernible on the skyline to the top-left.

SEVENOAKS [530550] [9-8-66]

Looking north with Knole Park to the right and the town centre occupying the centre of the picture. The large expanse of water to the top of the view has been enlarged out of the River Darent.

KNOLE HOUSE [539542] [29-6-53]

The full extent of Knole House, ¾ mile south-east of Sevenoaks, can best be appreciated from this early aerial view. Dating in parts from 1456, it is reputed to be one of the largest private houses in England.

IGHTHAM MOTE   [584534] [7-7-54]

Ightham Mote is truly a gem in the Kentish countryside. Dating mostly from 1340 it is one of our most romantic old houses. The word 'mote' refers to its use as an ancient place of assembly and not to the 'moat' which later came to surround the house.

WROTHAM   [615595] [29-5-78]

Vertical view showing the M20 motorway under construction. Wrotham village lies in the bottom-left corner, hemmed in between two motorways for the M26 has since been built to the south.

CHEVENING [485578] [29-6-53]

Looking north-west along the lake towards Chevening House. The house dates from 1616-30 and is relatively plain, but the landscaped grounds which surround it are magnificent, as shown here.

Areas

Finding the Missing Lengths by Dividing

Sorry — I thought you said de viking...

If you know the <u>area of a rectangle</u> and <u>one of the sides</u>, you can work out the <u>other side</u>. You just divide.

EXAMPLE: You know the <u>width × height = 80 cm²</u>. That means the height is <u>80 ÷ 10 = 8 cm</u>.

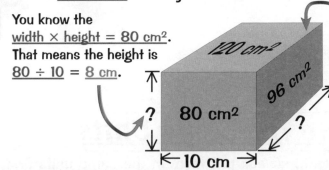

120 cm²

96 cm²

80 cm²

?

?

← 10 cm →

The <u>length × width = 120 cm²</u>. So the length is <u>120 ÷ 10 = 12 cm</u>.

Find the missing side lengths of these rectangles.

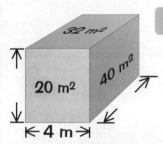

← 4 m →

8 m²

?

← 8m →

?

56 m²

← ? →

3 cm

27 cm²

← ? →

20 cm²

4 cm

Careful with those units — some are m, some are cm.

Find the missing side lengths of this box.

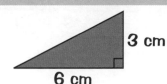

32 m²

40 m²

20 m²

← 4 m →

Height = ... Length = ...

A Right-Angled Triangle is Half a Rectangle

You can find out the area of a right-angled triangle by halving the area of a rectangle.

EXAMPLE:

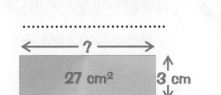

4 cm

8 cm

The area of this rectangle is <u>4 × 8 = 32 cm²</u>. So the area of the pink triangle is <u>half of 32 = 16 cm²</u>.

What are the areas of these triangles?

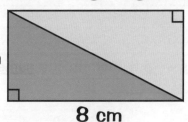

3 cm

6 cm

5 m

18 m

5 cm

4 cm

I've done it! I've finished the page.

Measurements

Just a couple to warm up with...

Alfredo's car has broken down 5 km from home.

How far is that in metres?

....

Alfredo decides to walk back. When he's walked 4000 m, how many km has he got left to walk?

....

Change Both into the Same Units

To <u>add or subtract</u> measurements, always put them in the <u>same units</u> first. If you don't, everything will just go <u>totally pear-shaped</u>.

Have a look at these facts about imperial units. You'll need some of them for these questions.

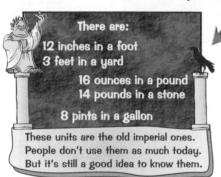

There are:

12 inches in a foot
3 feet in a yard

16 ounces in a pound
14 pounds in a stone

8 pints in a gallon

These units are the old imperial ones. People don't use them as much today. But it's still a good idea to know them.

Now have a go at this lot:

4.5 m – 80 cm = ...

18 inches – 1 foot = ...

3400 g + 4.6 kg = ...

3 ml + 6.45 l = ...

1300 m – 0.8 km = ...

Alfredo can walk 800 metres each day. But he's just bought some new shoes, and he can now walk 5 times as far in a day. How many kilometres can he walk each day in his new shoes?

....

....

It's the same with <u>comparing measurements</u> — put them in the <u>same units</u> first.

If you want to change smaller units to larger units, you've got to divide.

Multiplication's what you want to swap from larger units to smaller units.

Which is the larger amount in each pair:

10 g of butter or 1 kg of butter? ....

2 km of road or 3000 m of road? ....

30 millilitres of milk or 1 litre of milk? ....

5 gallons of slime or 41 pints of slime? ....

Measurements

Start by Measuring Something Easy

You can work out <u>really small</u> measurements by <u>measuring lots of them</u> and then dividing.
Or you could work out <u>big</u> measurements by <u>measuring one bit</u> and then multiplying.

EXAMPLE: How can I find the <u>weight of an ant</u>?

<u>Weigh 100 ants</u> — then <u>divide by 100</u>.

Suggest how to measure these things, then do it yourself.

The weight of one paper clip. Method: ....
.... Answer: ....

The thickness of a penny. Method: ....
.... Answer: ....

The thickness of a piece of paper. Method: ....
.... Answer: ....

Converting Imperial Units to Metric Units

OK, so you know what imperial units are now. It's really handy to be able to change from imperial units to metric units. Especially for recipes and things like that.

You can use a calculator for this bit.

EXAMPLE: I need half a pint of cream, but my measuring jug is only marked in ml. If 8 pints = 4.5 litres, what is half a pint, to the nearest 10 ml?

<u>8 pints = 4.5 litres</u>, so that's <u>4500 ml</u>. So 1 pint is <u>4500 ÷ 8 = 562.5 ml</u>.
That's <u>560 ml</u>, to the nearest 10 ml. So half a pint is <u>half of 560 ml</u>, which is <u>280 ml</u>.

Anna has an old recipe for the best ever Rat & Toad Pie. But she's a modern witch — she only likes metric units. Change the units in the recipe from imperial to metric units.

.... of water
.... of toad
.... of rat
.... of flour
.... pigeon eggs
.... of sickly sauce

RAT & TOAD PIE

Imperial
4 pints of water
3 ounces of toad
2 pounds of rat
12 ounces of flour
4 pigeon eggs
2 drops of sickly sauce

The Conversions:
1 ounce = 30 grams
1 pound = 0.45 kilograms
8 pints = 4.5 litres

The last two aren't in proper units anyway, so just leave them as they are.

Graphs, Charts and Tables

Understanding Bar Charts

A bar chart is a way of showing data so it's clear and easy to understand. The height of each bar shows the amount of something.

This chart shows the results of Broughton's Annual Chocolate-Eating Contest.

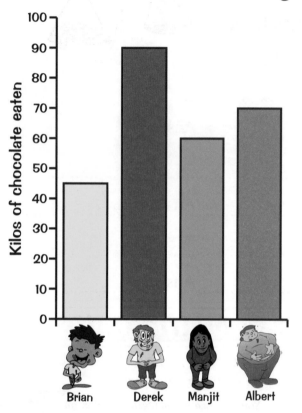

Try drawing a line from the top of each bar across to the number on the scale.

Okay, now for some questions...

Who ate the most chocolate?

....

How much chocolate was that?

....

How much did Brian eat?

....

Making and Reading Tally Charts

Kieran has been looking for escaped zoo animals on Breckby Moor. He recorded his findings with this tally chart.

How many animals in total did Kieran see?

....

How many leopards did Kieran see?

....

How many more giant rats were seen than orangutangs?

....

ANIMAL	TALLY
Leopard	JHT III
Bear	JHT
Orangutang	III
Giant Rat	JHT JHT JHT
Wildebeeste	JHT JHT II

Graphs, Charts and Tables

A <u>pictogram</u> is quite <u>similar</u> to a <u>bar chart</u>.
But it's the <u>number of pictures</u>, not the <u>height of the bar</u>, that shows the amount.

Pictograms are a Bit Like Bar Charts

The legendary Giant Toad of Furness has come out of hiding.
This week it has been eating cows.

= 1 cow

This shows what each picture means.

On which day did the toad eat the most cows?

....

Bar charts are usually best for big numbers, or for fractions and money. They save you drawing too much.

How many cows did the toad eat in total?

....

Making Frequency Tables and Tally Charts

Frequency tables show the totals of the tallies in a tally chart.
Complete this frequency table of cheese mountains on the moon.

CHEESE	TALLY	FREQUENCY
Stilton	JHT JHT JHT JHT I	
Cheddar	JHT JHT II	
Camembert	JHT JHT JHT I	
Garlic Roule	JHT III	
Wensleydale	JHT JHT JHT JHT IIII	

Choosing relatives — I PICKED A GRAN... *groan...*

Bar charts can be made from frequency tables, which can be made from tally charts.
They're all <u>different ways</u> of showing the <u>same thing</u>. And that's all there is to it.

Bar Charts

Each Bar Can Represent a Group

Instead of each bar of a bar chart representing <u>one thing</u>, it can show a <u>group of things</u>.

This bar chart shows the results of <u>Broughton Canoe Club's Annual Rat Race</u>.
Marks were awarded out of 40, for rattiness.

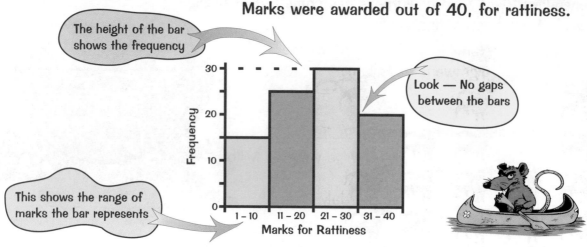

The height of the bar shows the frequency

Look — No gaps between the bars

This shows the range of marks the bar represents

What was the most common group of marks?

....

Just look for the highest bar.

How many rats entered the competition?

....

It's out of 40, so half marks will be 20.

Estimate how many got fewer than half marks.

....

....

I wanted to find out how many times my sheep go "baa" in an hour.
I counted them and put the results in this bar chart.

How many sheep were there?

....

Now that's what I call a BAA CHART...

I thought that more than half would "baa"
at least 11 times in an hour. Was I right?

....

....

Bar Charts? — thought you said BAR CARTS...

These are just like <u>ordinary bar charts</u> — but each bar is for a <u>group of things</u>, that's all.

Pie Charts

Understanding Pie Charts

Pie charts are really good at showing how much one thing is, compared with the rest.

EXAMPLE: This pie chart shows where some pigs went Truffle-Hunting on holiday.

Yum... truffle

Roughly what <u>fraction</u> of the pigs went to Millom?

Kirkby Moor

Millom

Grizedale Forest

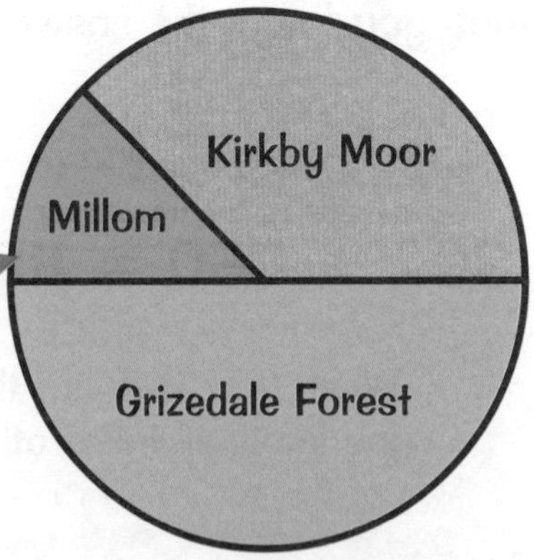

The Millom bit is about $\frac{1}{8}$ of the whole circle.
So roughly $\frac{1}{8}$ of the pigs went to Millom.

Roughly what fraction went to Grizedale Forest? ....

Roughly what fraction went to Kirkby Moor? ....

Here's another pie chart.
This one shows where the pigs <u>stayed</u> on their truffle-hunting holidays.

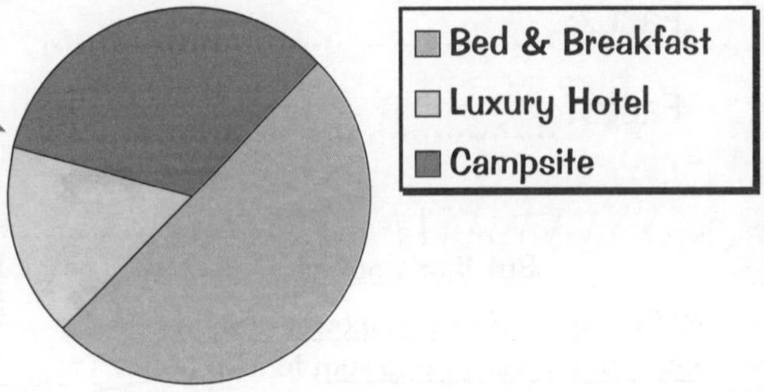

□ Bed & Breakfast
□ Luxury Hotel
■ Campsite

What <u>fraction</u> stayed on a campsite?

....

What <u>percentage</u> stayed in a luxury hotel?

....

....

And what <u>percentage</u> stayed in a bed & breakfast?

For these two, find the fraction, then turn it into a percentage.

....

....

If there were 24 pigs in total, how many stayed in a luxury hotel, like Porky here?

And how many stayed on a campsite?

Certainly, Porky.

A glass of your finest swill, please, waiter.

....

....

....

....

....

....

Calculations

Mental Calculation Strategies

Work Out *One Sum* Using *Another*

Addition and subtraction are <u>related</u>.
Once you know the answer to one sum, you know <u>three other things</u> too.

$$850 + 302 = 1152$$

$$302 + 850 = 1152$$

$$1152 - 850 = 302$$

$$1152 - 302 = 850$$

When you work out this <u>one sum</u>, you know all these other facts too.

Work out these sums, then write down the three other things the answer tells you.

5.98 + 2.53 = ...

Fact 1: ....

Fact 2: ....

Fact 3: ....

1005 – 454 = ...

Fact 1: ....

Fact 2: ....

Fact 3: ....

But <u>that's not all</u>.
With a <u>little bit</u> of <u>brainpower</u> you can <u>use the answer to one sum</u> to help you answer other sums with numbers that are <u>similar</u> but <u>not quite the same</u>.

EXAMPLE: <u>8421 – 1356 = 7065</u>.
So what is 8421 – 7066?

You know <u>8421 – 7065</u> is <u>1356</u>.
7066 is <u>1 more</u> than 7065, so take an <u>extra 1</u> off.
Which makes the answer <u>1355</u>.

Use the sum in the example to find answers quickly to these questions.

What is 7065 + 1360? ....

What is 8420 – 1356? ....

What is 8420 – 7070? ....

What is 1356 + 7062? ....

Laura collects bits of scrap paper from recycling bins. She has 477 at home and 692 at a friend's house. That's 1169 in total. This should help you answer these sums.

What is 1170 – 692? ....

What is 690 + 477? ....

What is 1169 – 475? ....

What is 480 + 692? ....

Mental Calculation Strategies

Adding up Multiples of Ten

You find <u>multiples of ten</u> in your ten times table — 10, 20, 30, 40, 50, 60 and so on. You can tell they're multiples of 10 because they <u>end in 0</u>.

It's <u>easy</u> to add up multiples of 10. All you do is <u>forget about the 0</u>, add them up like they're small numbers, then <u>stick the 0 back on</u> the end.

Do these sums in your head.

80 + 40 + 50 + 30 = ...

10 + 90 + 20 + 50 = ...

60 + 30 + 40 + 60 = ...

70 + 20 + 80 + 80 = ...

90 + 80 + 60 + 70 = ...

EXAMPLE:

80 + 70 + 40 + 90

Ignore the zeros for a moment and you've got a sum that's easy to do in your head.

8 + 7 + 4 + 9 = 28

Now simply stick the 0 back on the end and there's your answer. ☞**280**

Finding Pairs that add up to a Multiple of Ten

In the sums below, look for <u>pairs</u> that add up to a <u>multiple of 10</u>. If you do them first, it makes the rest of the sum easier.

EXAMPLE:

36 + 19 + 24

Looks tough. But 36 and 24 add up to 60. 60 + 19 is nice and easy. It's 79.

Use this method to work out these sums.

53 + 37 + 12 = ...   38 + 65 + 12 = ...

31 + ... + 29 = 78   14 + ... + 26 = 95

49 + 28 + 42 = ...   72 + 18 + 79 = ...

.... + 15 + 35 = 88   .... + 16 + 64 = 100

Starting with the Biggest Number

Or you could just start with the <u>biggest</u> number and <u>do it in your head</u>.

Charlene — what's 13 + 65 + 29?

Er...
65...
94...
107

It's 107, Mr Wallis.

It's easier to add a <u>little</u> number to a <u>big</u> one than the other way round.

Do these sums in your head.

70 + 15 + 14 = ...

21 + 88 + 12 = ...

19 + 14 + 92 = ...

Mental Calculation Strategies

Finding an Easier Way to do the Sum

There are <u>easy ways</u> and <u>difficult ways</u> to do things.
It's much easier to <u>drive</u> a car somewhere than <u>push</u> it.

It's often the same with <u>sums</u>. You can do it the hard way...
or you can be just a little bit <u>clever</u> and find an easier way.

EXAMPLE: 70 + 71 + 75 + 77

The hard way

> 70 and 71 is 141,
> 141 and 75 is, um, 216,
> 216 and 77 is, hang on...
> 293 — is that right?

> We've got four lots of 70.
> That's 280. And we've
> got 1, 5 and 7. That's 13.
> 280 and 13 is 293.

The easy way

This guy's doing:
 (70 x 4) + (1 + 5 + 7)
It's the same sum — but much easier.

Do these sums the easy way,
and explain how you did them.

63 + 64 + 61 + 59 = ...*247*....

This is how I did it *4 lots of 60 is 240. 3 + 4 + 1 – 1 is 7. 240 and 7 is 247.*

53 + 55 + 50 + 54 + 51 = ...

This is how I did it ....

90 + 93 + 89 = ...

This is how I did it ....

73 + 70 + 67 + 74 = ...

This is how I did it ....

40 + 42 + 41 + 44 + 43 = ...

This is how I did it ....

EXPLAIN YOURSELF, BILLY!

Just finishing my
tables, Mr Wallis.

79 + 83 + 82 + 85 = ...

This is how I did it ....

....

Mental Calculation Strategies

Adding and Subtracting Multiples of 100

You can tell something's a <u>multiple of 100</u> because it's got <u>00</u> at the end of it.

When you're <u>adding</u> or <u>subtracting</u> multiples of 100, follow these rules.

EXAMPLE: 5700 + 2500

1. Ignore the 00s.
2. Do the sum you're left with.
3. Stick 00 on the end of the answer.

→ That leaves 57 + 25.

→ 57 + 25 = 82.

→ So the answer is 8200.

007 — you're licensed to not be a multiple of 100.

I only wanted the football results...

EXAMPLE: 6200 – 3800

1. Ignore the 00s. That leaves 62 – 38.
2. Do the sum. 62 – 38 = 24.
3. Stick the 00 back on. Answer: 2400.

Follow the three rules to answer these questions.

4700 + 3800. What is the sum without the 00s? .... + ... = ...

Now stick the 00 back on the end of your answer ....

7300 – 2700. What is the sum without the 00s? .... – .... = ...

Now stick the 00 back on the end of your answer ....

2300 + 4900. What is the sum without the 00s? .... + ... = ...

Now stick the 00 back on the end of your answer ....

7600 – 3900. What is the sum without the 00s? .... – .... = ...

Now stick the 00 back on the end of your answer ....

Use the same method to fill in these blanks. Try to do them all in your head.

3200 + ... = 5100   .... + 5200 = 8900

.... – 8400 = 2800   10 100 – .... = 6000

9700 + ... = 12 500   .... – 4600 = 2500

Column Addition

Use Carrying to Add Big Numbers

Carrying lets you add big numbers really easily. It doesn't matter how big they are, or how many there are. All you need to remember is to keep the numbers in the right columns. And add the columns in the right order — units first, then tens, then hundreds, and so on.

EXAMPLE:

```
  7364
+ 6879
 14243
  1 1 1
```

Add the units. 4 + 9 is 13.
Write 3 in the units column and carry 1 to the tens.

Add the tens. 6 + 7 is 13, and + the 1 you carried is 14.
Write 4 in the tens column and carry 1 to the hundreds.

Add the hundreds. 3 + 8 is 11, and + the 1 you carried is 12.
Write 2 in the hundreds column, and carry 1 to the thousands.

Add the thousands. 7 + 6 is 13, + the 1 you carried is 14.
There's nothing more left to add, so write in the 14.

Use carrying to add up these numbers.

```
   5743          4975          8642          4534
 + 7869        + 2645        + 5979        + 5724
 _____        _____        _____        _____

 _____        _____        _____        _____


     21           424         26991          5283
  14596          5586         33492            87
      6           564             2         45533
   7532            97            12          9602
 +  977        + 5312        +  864        +  790
 _____        _____        _____        _____

 _____        _____        _____        _____
```

Drop everything — we've got things to carry...

This method works for any numbers you choose, so you can add huge numbers without it really getting any harder. You need to carry when the column adds to 10 or more.

Column Subtraction

Use Borrowing to Subtract Big Numbers

Borrowing lets you subtract big numbers from each other <u>really easily</u>.

EXAMPLE:

$$\begin{array}{r} 9345 \\ -\ 2892 \\ \hline 3 \end{array}$$

Here's the sum: 9345 – 2892.
First subtract the <u>units</u>.
This is easy. 5 – 2 is 3.
Write 3 in the units column.

> We've borrowed 1 from the 3 in the hundreds column. So we cross out the 3 and write 2.

$$\begin{array}{r} {}^{2\ 14} \\ 9\cancel{3}45 \\ -\ 2892 \\ \hline 53 \end{array}$$

Subtract the <u>tens</u>. This is trickier, because 9 is bigger than 4.
No problem — we'll borrow a 1 from the column to the left,
the hundreds column. Now the sum is 14 – 9, which is 5.
And because we've borrowed 1 from the hundreds,
we only have 2 of them left.

> We've borrowed 1 from the 9 in the thousands column. So we cross out the 9 and write 8.

$$\begin{array}{r} {}^{8\ 12\ 14} \\ \cancel{9}\cancel{3}45 \\ -\ 2892 \\ \hline 453 \end{array}$$

Subtract the <u>hundreds</u>. 8 is bigger than 2, so we borrow again.
Borrow 1 from the thousands. Now the sum is 12 – 8 = 4.
And because we've borrowed 1 from the 9 in the thousands,
we've only got 8 thousands left.

$$\begin{array}{r} {}^{8\ 12\ 14} \\ \cancel{9}\cancel{3}45 \\ -\ 2892 \\ \hline 6453 \end{array}$$

Finally, subtract the <u>thousands</u>.
Another easy one. 8 – 2 is 6.
Write 6 in the thousands column.
And there's the answer — 6453.

Hello, my name's Colin

Didn't you say "Wheelbarrow a wand from the Colin to the lift"?

Use borrowing to do these subtraction sums.

$$\begin{array}{r} 7625 \\ -\ 3098 \\ \hline \end{array} \qquad \begin{array}{r} 6123 \\ -\ 2204 \\ \hline \end{array} \qquad \begin{array}{r} 9427 \\ -\ 2882 \\ \hline \end{array}$$

$$\begin{array}{r} 784651 \\ -\ 1573 \\ \hline \end{array} \qquad \begin{array}{r} 209427 \\ -\ 4867 \\ \hline \end{array} \qquad \begin{array}{r} 527625 \\ -\ 6108 \\ \hline \end{array} \qquad \begin{array}{r} 46123 \\ -\ 4248 \\ \hline \end{array}$$

I need to lie down after that appalling joke...

With subtracting, you need to <u>borrow</u> a 1 from the column to the left if the top digit is smaller than the bottom digit. Learn the method above and carry on laughing.

Solving Problems

Addition and Subtraction Problems

Some Super Pop Questions

To answer these real life questions you'll have to <u>add</u> numbers using <u>carrying</u>, or <u>subtract</u> them using <u>borrowing</u>, like you did on the last two pages.

EXAMPLE: 9854 people were asked which girl band they preferred — the Borrs, or Bewildered. 6269 said Bewildered. How many preferred The Borrs?

The Borrs
Very Boring

Includes their chart-topping hits
"So dull", "Runaway while you can"

It's a <u>subtraction</u> sum, so take 6269 away from 9854.

Answer — <u>3585</u>.

$$\begin{array}{r} {\scriptstyle 7\ 14\ 14} \\ 9\cancel{8}\cancel{5}\cancel{4} \\ -\ 6269 \\ \hline 3585 \end{array}$$

Say you will Say to Me Celery...

Do the sums — and show your working out — to answer these questions.

So, 6269 people liked Bewildered and 3585 preferred The Borrs. How many more people liked Bewildered?

Write the sum and answer in this space

....

I'm Super Pointing Finger Man.

The Superhero Association has a vacancy for a new superhero — <u>Super Pointing Finger Man</u>. The 3 shortlisted applicants were given 1 second to point at as many objects as they could. The results were: Fred 7352, Rolf 3947, and Jerry 14 742.

No — I'm Super Pointing Finger Man

How many points were made altogether?

Rubbish. I'm Super Pointing Finger Man!

....

How many more points did Fred make than Rolf?

....

How many more points did Jerry make than Fred and Rolf put together?

....

Checking Results

Use a Calculator to Check Results

The sums you've been doing on the last three pages are <u>pretty difficult</u>.
But it's important that you learn to do them <u>without</u> a calculator.

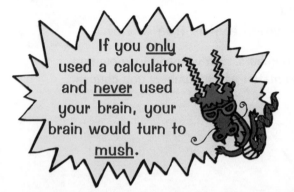

If you <u>only</u> used a calculator and <u>never</u> used your brain, your brain would turn to <u>mush</u>.

It's still a good idea to check the sums by doing them on your calculator.
If the calculator says a <u>different</u> answer to the one you got, try doing the sum yourself <u>again</u>.

Do the sums yourself then use a calculator to check the answer.

$$475$$
$$12527$$
$$19$$
$$34728$$
$$1274$$

Write down the
answer from the
calculator

....

Add up the sum yourself, then type this into your calculator:
475 + 12 527 + 19 + 34 728 + 1274 =
If you get different answers, you've made a mistake somewhere.

$$571432$$
$$- 4974$$

Now write down the
answer from the
calculator

....

Derek has discovered how to grow money on trees. He has three trees and they grow £3792, £5874 and £10 923. What's the total amount of money grown? ....

What does the calculator say? ....

But he has to pay £1786 to a security guard to stop people stealing his money. How much does he have left? ....

What does the calculator say?

....

Numbers and the Number System	# Odd and Even Numbers

You don't just have to follow boring methods on this page — you get to use your head.

Making Rules for Odd and Even Numbers

EXAMPLE: "The product of 2 odd numbers is odd".
Investigate this statement and decide whether it is true or not.

$3 \times 7 = 21$ ✓
ODD   ODD   ODD

It's true for these numbers. But we need to know that it's always true, no matter which numbers you choose.

Let's try bigger numbers: $27 \times 13 = 351$ ✓
     ODD   ODD   ODD

Let's try numbers with different numbers of digits: $343 \times 3 = 1029$ ✓
               ODD   ODD   ODD

Well, I can't find any numbers which won't give an odd number answer.
So I think it has to be <u>TRUE</u>.

Now it's your turn. For each of these statements, decide whether it's true.
If you think it is, give three examples which agree with it.
If you think it's false, give one example where it doesn't work.

The product of three odd numbers is odd.	....
	....

Two even numbers multiplied together give an odd number.	....
	....

Complete these statements by writing "odd" or "even" in the spaces.

If you multiply any two even numbers, you always get an .... number.

The product of an .... number and an .... number is always odd.

The product of two even numbers and an odd number is ....

Write the numbers below as twice a number plus one.

All <u>odd numbers</u> can be written as <u>twice a number plus one</u>.

21 is *twice 10 plus 1*   17 is ....

49 is ....   101 is ....

67 is ....   83 is ....

Properties of Numbers

Divisibility and Factors

Ha ha! I'm the divisible man!

Divisibility is about whether you can divide one number by another and not get a remainder.

48 is divisible by 12 because 48 ÷ 12 is 4, no remainder.
48 is not divisible by 10 because 48 ÷ 10 is 4 remainder 8.

Some more silly words... that means 48 is a multiple of 12.
But 48 is not a multiple of 10.

And 12 is a factor of 48. But 10 is not a factor of 48.

No, he's the invisible man.
He gets confused, poor chap.

EXAMPLE: Paint a big orange splodge behind the numbers that are divisible by 25.

257   **805**   **2152**

975   **1001**   **525**   **3100**   **1650**

A number is divisible by 25 if the last two digits are 00, 25, 50 or 75.

That question could also have said paint a big orange splodge behind the numbers that are multiples of 25 — or numbers that have 25 as a factor. They mean the same thing.

Draw a ring around the right numbers in these questions.

Which of these numbers are divisible by 3?

513   413   1527   3336
(213)   313   1627

Example: 213. Sum of digits 2 + 1 + 3 = 6.
6 is divisible by 3.

A number is divisible by 3 if the sum of its digits is divisible by 3.

Which of these numbers are multiples of 8?

7887   4608   9536
(5592)   1888   2396   2050

Example: 5592. Last 3 digits 592 are divisible by 8.
Half of it is 2796, which is divisible by 4.

A number is divisible by 8 if half of it is divisible by 4, or if the last three digits are divisible by 8.

Which of these numbers have 9 as a factor?

9855   1818   8586
(3249)   1919   9495   8584

Example: 3249. Sum of digits 3 + 2 + 4 + 9 = 18.
18 is divisible by 9.

A number is divisible by 9 if the sum of its digits is divisible by 9.

Which of these numbers are multiples of 6?

426   126   3526
226   326   3524   3528

A number is divisible by 6 if it is even and also divisible by 3.

Properties of Numbers

Problems with Factors and Multiples

Remember — a <u>multiple</u> of a number is one which can be divided by it with <u>no remainder</u>.
24 ÷ 8 is 3, no remainder. So 24 is a mutiple of 8. And 8 is a factor of 24.

EXAMPLE: Beanthwaite Safari Park lines up its <u>elephants</u> in a pattern — <u>five brown</u>
elephants, <u>four blue</u> elephants, five brown, four blue, and so on.

What colour is the <u>76th elephant</u>? Well, five and four elephants is <u>nine</u> in total.

So think of a number close to 76 that is a <u>multiple of 9</u>. A good one is <u>72</u> — 72 is 9 × 8.
Now we know that the <u>72nd elephant</u> is the last of four <u>blue</u> ones. The 73rd must be brown.
So must the 74th, 75th, 76th and 77th — and the 78th, 79th, 80th and 81st are blue.

Answer — the <u>76th elephant</u> is <u>brown</u>.

> Use multiples to help you answer these questions.

What colour is the 62nd elephant? ....

What colour is the 109th elephant? ....

What position in line is the 17th blue elephant? ....

....

The last one is <u>really tricky</u>.
Here's a clue to get you started:

The 1st blue elephant is in the 1st group of blue, the
5th blue elephant is in the 2nd group of blue, the 9
is in the 3rd group of blue. So where is the 17th?

Then work out the position of this group in the line.
Good luck!

Finding the Smallest Common Multiple

Remember — the multiples of a particular number are all the numbers in its times table.
So the <u>smallest common multiple</u> of two numbers is the smallest number you'd find in
the times tables of both numbers.

EXAMPLE: What's the <u>smallest common multiple</u> of 12 and 16?

Go through the multiples of 16 until you find one which is in the 12 times table too.

16 × 1 is 16. That's <u>not</u> a multiple of 12. 16 × 2 is 32. That's <u>not</u> a multiple of 12.
But 16 × 3 is 48 and that <u>is</u> a multiple of 12. So <u>48</u> is the smallest common multiple.

> Use multiples to help you answer these questions.

What's the lowest common multiple of 6 and 8? ....

What's the lowest common multiple of 6 and 15? ....

What's the lowest common multiple of 8 and 12? ....

HINT

It's quicker if you go
through the multiples
of the bigger number.

Properties of Numbers

Square Numbers

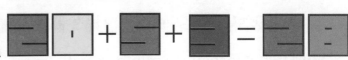

I know they're numbers and I know they're square, but it's still not what I mean by square numbers.

A <u>square number</u> is what you get when you <u>multiply</u> a number <u>by itself</u>.

"<u>Six squared</u>" means 6×6. It's usually written as 6^2 — the little ^{2} means "<u>squared</u>".

Fill in the gaps in this list of square numbers.

$1^2 = \underline{\;\;1\;\;}$ $4^2 = \underline{\;\;\;\;\;\;}$ $7^2 = \underline{\;\;49\;\;}$ $10^2 = \underline{\;\;\;\;\;\;}$

$2^2 = \underline{\;\;4\;\;}$ $5^2 = \underline{\;\;25\;\;}$ $8^2 = \underline{\;\;\;\;\;\;}$ $11^2 = \underline{\;\;121\;\;}$

$3^2 = \underline{\;\;\;\;\;\;}$ $6^2 = \underline{\;\;\;\;\;\;}$ $9^2 = \underline{\;\;81\;\;}$ $12^2 = \underline{\;\;\;\;\;\;}$

Work out these square numbers.

$15^2 = \underline{\;\;15 \times 15\;\;} = \underline{\;\;225\;\;}$ $18^2 = \underline{\;\;\;\;\;\;\;\;\;} = \underline{\;\;\;\;\;\;}$

$21^2 = \underline{\;\;21 \times 21\;\;} = \underline{\;\;\;\;\;\;}$ $30^2 = \underline{\;\;\;\;\;\;\;\;\;} = \underline{\;\;\;\;\;\;}$

Sometimes you'll have to look at square numbers the <u>other way round</u>. Instead of getting asked "what is 15^2?", you might get asked something like this — what number, <u>multiplied by itself</u>, gives 225? The answer is <u>15</u> — because $15^2 = 225$.

You'll need a calculator to do these questions.

What number, multiplied by itself, gives 2809? .....

What number, multiplied by itself, gives 4356? .....

What number, multiplied by itself, gives 7921? .....

What number, multiplied by itself, gives 3364? .....

What number, multiplied by itself, gives 5476? .....

The area of a square is 256 cm².

What is the length of each of the sides? .....

The area of a square is 529 cm².

What is the length of each of the sides? .....

Confused? Don't worry. Here's how to do it. First <u>make a guess</u>. Try, say, 50×50. That's 2500, so it must be <u>more than 50</u>. Now try, say, 55×55. That's 3025, so it must be <u>less than 55</u>. Try 53×53. And hey presto, you get 2809. So <u>53</u> is the <u>answer</u>. Keep on guessing till you get it right.

Reasoning about Numbers

Number Problems and Puzzles and Stuff

You'll need a calculator and guesswork to help you with these questions.

Find two consecutive numbers with a

product of 9506: .... and ....

Find two consecutive numbers with a

product of 3080: .... and ....

> Consecutive numbers are ones that come next to each other, like 45 and 46, or 67 and 68.

Fill in the gaps.   ◯④◯ × ◯◯ = ②⓪⑦⓪④

Here's one to get you thinking — write down all the 3-digit numbers you can think of with digits that add up to 23. I've done a couple to get you started.

599, 689,

....

....

> Try to work out some method for finding them.

> Yeah, or you'll never know when you've got them all.

How many are there in total? ....

No calculators allowed for solving this multiplication table puzzle, I'm afraid — but it's not hard if you know your times tables.

You have to fill in the blank squares. Don't fret, it's not as tricky as it looks.

Start with the ones you've got the most clues for — you know that if 2 times something is 6, the something must be 3.

So 3 goes here.

Every time you fill in another square, you've got more clues to work from. You should be able to fill in every one.

×	2		7	
	6	12		
5	10			
	12			48
				72

Right, let's see if you can crack my secret code. Each letter from A to G is a code for one of these digits — 0, 1, 2, 3, 4, 6, 8.

$C \times C = GC$ $D \times D = AC$ $D \times C = ED$

$C + C = AE$ $D + D = B$ $C + D = AF$

A is ......, B is ......, C is ......, D is ......, E is ......, F is ......, G is ....

Reasoning about Numbers

More Puzzles and Some Nice Patterns

Here's a brain-teaser — it might take you a while to figure this one out.

Use the digits 1, 2, 3, 4, 5 and 6 to
fill in the empty circles in this sum.
You can only put one digit in each circle, and you can only use each digit once.

$$\bigcirc \times \bigcirc\bigcirc = \bigcirc\bigcirc\bigcirc$$

Make a formula to work out numbers in a number sequence.

In pattern 1 there are _4_ balls.

In pattern 2 there are _7_ balls.

In pattern 3 there are ___ balls.

1   2   3

How are those numbers related?

Pattern 1: _4_ = 1 + _3_

Pattern 2: _7_ = 1 + _6_

Pattern 3: ___ = 1 + ___

You should notice something about the numbers that you're adding to 1 each time.
Notice how they're related to the pattern number. And use that to make a formula.

Number of balls in pattern N = 1 + ...

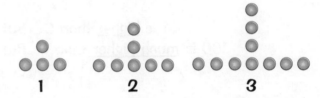

If you've got the formula right,
you should be able to <u>replace N</u>
with the number <u>1</u> and get <u>4 balls</u>.
Or replace N with the number <u>2</u>
and get <u>7 balls</u>. And so on.

So in pattern 8 there are ___ balls.

And in pattern 15 there are ___ balls.

Here's a square. Draw
straight lines to divide it
into six smaller squares.

This is half of a shape. What might the whole
shape have looked like? I've drawn one for you.
Draw two more that could be the whole shape.

<u>Hint</u> - the smaller squares
are <u>not all the same size</u>.

Half shape

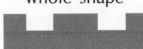

One possible
whole shape

Place Value, Order and Rounding

Ordering Negative Numbers

Negative numbers are <u>below zero</u>.
You can tell they're negative because
they've got a <u>minus sign</u> in front of them.

It's no use, we'll never be able to do it.

I don't know why we even bother trying.

"Negative numbers"

Remember that with negative numbers,
the order is <u>all topsy-turvy</u>. The
higher a number would be if it was
<u>positive</u>, the <u>lower</u> it is when it's
negative.

4 is <u>higher</u> than 3. But –4 is <u>lower</u> than –3.
100 is <u>much higher</u> than 1. But –100 is <u>much lower</u> than –1.

Put these sets of integers in order, lowest first.

–7, –48, 26, 2, –2   ....

45, –13, 12, –14, –4   ....

–33, –35, 31, 39, –37   ....

Remember, <u>all</u> negative numbers are lower than <u>even the lowest</u> positive number.

Make a list of pairs of numbers that add up to 17.

● and ■ add up to 17. What could ● and ■ be?

17 and *0*		and	
8 and *9*		and	
–3 and *20*		and	
... and ...		and	
... and ...		and	
... and ...		and	
... and ...		and	
... and ...		and	
... and ...		and	

If you <u>only</u> use <u>positive</u> numbers, there aren't that many answers to this one.

But if you use <u>negative numbers</u> too, there are <u>loads</u> of possible answers.

You can't write <u>all</u> of them here. But you should be able to think of enough to fill in <u>all the spaces</u>.

Place Value, Order and Rounding

Negative Numbers and Temperature

-20 -15 -10 -5   0   5   10   15   20   25   30 °C

You'll come across <u>negative numbers</u> a lot when you're talking about <u>temperature</u>... Well, you will in <u>winter</u>, at least.

Because negative numbers are below zero, negative temperatures are <u>really cold</u>. The lower the temperature, the colder it is.

Answer these temperature questions.

It's –7 °C and the temperature falls by another

three degrees. How cold is it now? ....

It's –4 °C and it gets warmer by ten degrees. What's the new temperature? ....

Starting at 1 °C, the temperature drops by 12 degrees. What is it now? ....

It's –20 °C today and there's no way I'm going outside until it gets up to –5 °C.

By how much does the temperature have to rise for me to go outside? ....

How much must temperature fall from 10 °C to get to –10 °C? ....

Mon	Tue	Wed	Thu	Fri	Sat	Sun
–2 °C	5 °C	–5 °C	–4 °C	2 °C	–3 °C	0 °C

Derek accidentally booked his summer holiday to Iceland instead of Ibiza. The table shows the highest point the temperature reached on each day.

Plot the data on this line graph.

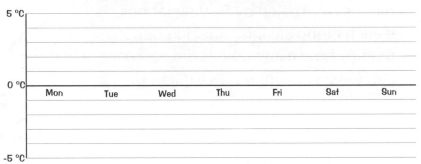

Calculations

Division — Answering in Fractions

Give the Quotient as a Fraction

Often when you divide one whole number by another, it doesn't go exactly.

👉 21 divided by 7 goes <u>exactly 3 times</u>.
But 21 ÷ 8 doesn't go exactly.
It goes <u>two and a bit</u> times.

Quotient is a daft maths word.
It means what you get when you
divide one number by another.

You might write that sum as 21 ÷ 8 = <u>2 remainder 5</u>. But there's another way of doing it.

$$21 \div 8 = 2\frac{5}{8}$$

Here's a good way of thinking about it. Write the division as an <u>improper fraction</u> first.

$$21 \div 8 = \frac{21}{8}$$ $\frac{21}{8}$ is $\frac{16+5}{8}$, and $\frac{16}{8}$ is 2 $\frac{21}{8} = 2\frac{5}{8}$

Do these division sums and write the quotient as a fraction.

27 ÷ 5 = ...　　50 ÷ 9 = ...　　42 ÷ 4 = ...

40 ÷ 7 = ...　　43 ÷ 7 = ...　　52 ÷ 6 = ...

90 ÷ 8 = ...　　52 ÷ 4 = ...　　75 ÷ 10 = ...

45 ÷ 4 = ...　　45 ÷ 4 = ...　　23 ÷ 3 = ...

111 ÷ 10 = ...　　89 ÷ 9 = ...　　72 ÷ 5 = ...

34 ÷ 3 = ...　　65 ÷ 6 = ...　　47 ÷ 6 = ...

In one of my dreams last night, 47 flying
rabbits were eaten by 5 flying hippos.
If each hippo ate the same number of
rabbits, how many rabbits did each one
eat? Give your answer as a fraction.

....

Division — Answering in Decimals | Calculations

Give the Quotient as a Decimal

The other way you can write the answer to a division is as a <u>decimal</u>.

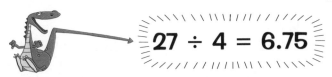

27 ÷ 4 = 6.75

If you wrote this as a <u>fraction</u>, it would be $6\frac{3}{4}$.

This is the way your <u>calculator</u> displays the
answer when you get it to do a division sum.
Go on, give it a try. Type in 27 ÷ 4 = and I bet you it will say 6.75.

> You should be able to do these in your head. Write the answers as decimals.

50 ÷ 4 = ...　　13 ÷ 2 = ...　　15 ÷ 2 = ...

98 ÷ 10 = ...　　46 ÷ 10 = ...　　33 ÷ 4 = ...

45 ÷ 4 = ...　　535 ÷ 100 = ...　　77 ÷ 10 = ...

> These are a bit trickier, so use a calculator.

674 ÷ 8 = ...

498 ÷ 4 = ...

358 ÷ 8 = ...

412 ÷ 5 = ...

169 ÷ 9 = ...

851 ÷ 12 = ...

642 ÷ 9 = ...

724 ÷ 8 = ...

196 ÷ 5 = ...

Sometimes you'll get a <u>really long</u> answer
on your calculator — usually when dividing
by an awkward number like 7 or 9.
<u>Round</u> the answer to <u>one decimal place</u>.

You need to look at the <u>second digit</u>
after the decimal point.

If it's 0, 1, 2, 3 or 4, simply <u>ignore it</u>
and all the numbers after it.

63.1458693 rounds to <u>63.1</u>

If it's 5, 6, 7, 8 or 9, <u>increase</u> the value
of the <u>first decimal place</u> by 1.

63.1528464 rounds to <u>63.2</u>

Five flying hippos — can I quotient you on that...

Quotient is just the fancy name for what you get when you divide by a number.
You can write it as a fraction or a decimal. Your calculator will give it as a decimal.
Remember — sometimes you need to round off the answer from your calculator.

Calculations

Division — Rounding Answers

Rounding after Division

Division sums often give you an answer that <u>isn't a whole number</u>.
But sometimes the question obviously <u>needs</u> a whole number as an answer.

EXAMPLE: Alan has £1530. A plane ticket
to Brisbane costs £425.

How many tickets can he buy?

$$\underline{1530 \div 425 = 3.6}$$

But 0.6 of a plane ticket isn't much use.
You have to buy a <u>whole number</u>. Alan doesn't have
enough to buy 4 tickets. So the answer is <u>3</u>.
That's an example of <u>rounding down</u>.

You only paid for 0.6 of a ticket and we're 0.6 of the way there, so we'll have to drop you off here.

A a a a r g g h h

The question won't tell you whether to round <u>up</u> or <u>down</u>.
You have to use your <u>common sense</u>.

All these questions need a whole number for an answer.
Use common sense to decide if you round up or down.

Use your calculator
when you need it.

1150 kangaroos have booked flights from London to
Brisbane with Wombat Airlines to see Slippy the
Boxing Roo defend his World Title. Each plane can
hold 184 kangaroos. How many planes will Wombat
Airlines need to get all of them to Brisbane?

....

Each of these boxes holds 15 ready-made airline meals.
How many boxes will be needed to feed 184 passengers?

....

87 passengers think the airline meal is so horrible they don't eat it.
How many boxes can be <u>completely</u> filled with the uneaten meals?

....

Brisbane Airport charges a £976 fee for every plane which lands there.
How many planes can Wombat Airlines land with £3542?

....

Brisbane Airport also charges a 35p fee for every house which lands
there. How many houses can Dorothy land if she has £5.45?

....

Quick Ways for Calculations

Split Up Two Digit Numbers to Multiply Them

Here's a reminder of a <u>handy trick</u> you already know — when you're multiplying a <u>two-digit</u> number, multiply the <u>units and tens separately</u>, and then add them together.

EXAMPLE: $94 \times 8 = \overset{\text{Tens}}{90} \times 8 + \overset{\text{Units}}{4} \times 8$

$$= 720 + 32 = 752$$

Here are a few questions for you to practise on.

$49 \times 7 = \underset{40 \times 7}{\dots\dots} + \underset{9 \times 7}{\dots\dots} = \dots\dots + \dots\dots = \dots\dots$

$56 \times 4 = \dots\dots + \dots\dots = \dots\dots + \dots\dots = \dots\dots$

$88 \times 8 = \dots\dots + \dots\dots = \dots\dots + \dots\dots = \dots\dots$

Now for some <u>good news</u> — you can use <u>exactly the same</u> trick to multiply a <u>decimal</u>. Only this time, instead of splitting the number into tens and units, split it into <u>units</u> and <u>tenths</u>.

EXAMPLE: $9.4 \times 8 = \overset{\text{Units}}{9} \times 8 + \overset{\text{Tenths}}{0.4} \times 8$

To do 9.4 × 8, split 9.4 into
<u>9 and 0.4</u>. Multiply them <u>both</u> by 8.
Then <u>add</u> the answers together.

$$= 72 + 3.2 = 75.2$$

Split these numbers up into units and tenths to make the sums easier.

$7.4 \times 6 = \dots\dots + \dots\dots = \dots\dots + \dots\dots = \dots\dots$

$9.3 \times 5 = \dots\dots + \dots\dots = \dots\dots + \dots\dots = \dots\dots$

$3.1 \times 7 = \dots\dots + \dots\dots = \dots\dots + \dots\dots = \dots\dots$

$8.7 \times 9 = \dots\dots + \dots\dots = \dots\dots + \dots\dots = \dots\dots$

$5.6 \times 8 = \dots\dots + \dots\dots = \dots\dots + \dots\dots = \dots\dots$

Maurice Moose really impressed the judges with his unique style in the Moose Skating World Championships. All 9 judges awarded him 9.8 points. How much did he score in total?

....

Calculations	# Fractions as Division

OK, hold it right there. Don't go any further until you've done these questions:

What is $\frac{1}{5}$ of 60? ....   What is $\frac{1}{3}$ of 21? ....

What is $\frac{1}{4}$ of 100? ....   What is $\frac{1}{10}$ of 70? ....

See — that wasn't too painful. You can find a fraction of something by <u>dividing</u>.
So if you <u>know</u> that 20 ÷ 5 = 4, you <u>also</u> know that $\frac{1}{5}$ of 20 is 4.

A Silly Football Question

EXAMPLE: My dad likes football. He eats <u>3 chocolate footballs</u> every day.
After <u>5 days</u> he has eaten <u>15 footballs</u>. What is $\frac{1}{5}$ of <u>15 footballs</u>?

It's easy. 5 lots of 3 footballs is 15 footballs (5 × 3 = 15).
So 15 ÷ 5 = 3. Which means $\frac{1}{5}$ of 15 = 3. So the answer is 3 footballs.

Your turn now:

If 5 × 20 = 100,
then what is $\frac{1}{5}$ of 100? ....   What about $\frac{1}{2}$ of 100? ....

My dad dreams about football 7 times every night.
After 30 days, that's 210 football dreams.

What is $\frac{1}{7}$ of 210? ....

What is $\frac{1}{3}$ of 210? ....

"Of" means "Times"

$\frac{1}{2}$ is the same as 1 ÷ 2.

YOU'LL NEED A CALCULATOR FOR THIS BIT.

 1 ÷ 2 =

Type it in on the <u>calculator</u>, and you should get: **0.5**

Multiplying by <u>0.5</u> is the same thing as finding a <u>half</u>.

"What is $\frac{1}{2}$ of 50?" means the same as "what is 0.5 times 50?"

It's the same for other fractions — to work out $\frac{1}{5}$ of something, do 1 ÷ 5 and times by that.

What is $\frac{1}{2}$ of 580?	What is $\frac{3}{4}$ of 420?	What is $\frac{1}{4}$ of 760?

580 × 0.5 = ...   420 × 0.75 = ...   760 × .... = ...

MATHS CLASSBOOK 6B

Doing Decimals in Your Head

Calculations

OK, you know by now how to add decimal numbers. But it's a bit harder when you do them <u>in your head</u>. So just remember these 3 easy steps, and it'll be a whole lot easier.

You <u>Double</u> Decimals Like <u>Normal Numbers</u>

Just 3 easy steps to learn:

1) Take the decimal point <u>out</u>.
2) <u>Do</u> the sum.
3) Put the decimal point <u>back in</u>.

What is double 1.12?

Take out the decimal point.	*112*
Do the sum.	*double 112 = 224*
Put the point back in.	*2.24*

Remember those steps...

What is double 3.5?

Do these in your head:

What is double 1.7?

It's the same with halving. Halve a go at this:

What is double 4.3?

What is half of 6.42?

....

<u>And</u> it's the same with <u>multiplying</u> by other numbers — same <u>three easy steps</u>, that's all.

What is 0.9 × 3?

Take out the point.	*9*
Do the sum.	*9 × 3 = 27*
Put the point back.	*2.7*

What is 0.5 × 7?

What is 0.6 × 8?

What is 0.4 × 5?

What is 1.4 × 10?

What is 3.65 × 10?

What is 3.65 × 100?

What is 1.9 × 100?

What is 0.7 × 10?

What is 0.08 × 10?

Do decimals in my head? — But decimals do my head in...

Decimals look pretty scary. That's why it's best to get rid of the decimal point before you do anything much with them. Make sure you put it back afterwards, and it'll be fine.

| Calculations | # Written Methods for Multiplication |

The best way to do a tricky multiplication is to <u>approximate</u> first.
You know how to approximate — just round both numbers off before you do the sum.

Approximate _the Answer First_

EXAMPLE: I'm going to try 322 × 96. (Wish me luck...)

322 is about 320, and
96 is about 100. So:

322 × 96 is approximately 320 × 100, which is 32 000.

Your turn, now.

That's the easy bit done — it's <u>about 32 000</u>.

279 × 11 is about _280_ × _10_ = ...

457 × 92 is about .... × .... = ...

634 × 83 is about .... × .... = ...

Multiply _each Digit_ Separately

(hee hee)

The next part's a <u>bit more tricky</u>. Well, it would be — but I know a quick way.
Split both numbers into <u>hundreds</u>, <u>tens</u> and <u>units</u>, <u>multiply separately</u>, then add them all up.

322 goes at the top...

... and 96 goes down the side...

	300	20	2
90	27 000	1800	180
6	1800	120	12

```
  28 980
+  1 932
  _____
  30 912
  1 1  1
```

... then I add up all the bits here...

... and the total goes here.

	200	70	9
10	....	....	....
1	....	....	....

....
+ ....
  ....

279 × 11 = ...

You've already worked out approximate answers
for these three, at the top of the page.

	600	30	4
80	....	....	....
3	....	....	....

....
+ ....

634 × 83 = ...

	400	50	7
90	....	....	....
2	....	....	....

....
+ ....

457 × 92 = ...

Written Methods for Division

Yes, you've guessed it — more approximating. And it's so easy your cat could do it.

Er...
I think
not.

Round the Numbers then do the Division

Roughly, what is 589 ÷ 32?   *589 ÷ 32 is about 600 ÷ 30, which is 20.*

Find approximate answers to all of these division sums:

396 ÷ 11 is about .... ÷ .... = ...

504 ÷ 19 is about .... ÷ .... = ...

928 ÷ 27 is about .... ÷ .... = ...

Divide by Subtracting Multiples

What is 589 ÷ 32?   Now I need the **exact** answer. So here's what I need to do:

① Work out some easy multiples of 32, like 10 × 32 or 5 × 32, and write them down.

② Subtract multiples until I get a number that's less than 32.

Easy multiples of 32
$32 \times 10 = 320$
$32 \times 5 = 160$
$32 \times 2 = 64$

Take them away from 589:
$589 - 320 = 269$
$269 - 160 = 109$
$109 - 64 = 45$
$45 - 32 = 13$

I've taken away 10 lots of 32, then 5 lots, then 2, then another 1.
That's 10 + 5 + 2 + 1 = 18. And there's 13 left.
So 589 ÷ 32 = 18 remainder 13. Which is nearly 20, as I guessed earlier. Bingo.

Check the answer's close to your approximation at the top of the page.

Find the exact answers to these division sums, by subtracting multiples.

396 ÷ 11	504 ÷ 19	928 ÷ 27
....	....	....
....	....	....
....	....	....
....	....	....
....	....	....

Solving Problems

Real Life Problems

Welcome to Furness Towers

The latest attraction everyone's talking about is Cumbria's very own <u>Furness Towers</u>.

Paul, Noel and Joel decide to spend the day there.

Furness Towers
The day out with a difference

See Flossybot Parsons, duckling extraordinaire.

There's something for everyone in Furness...

- *marvel at the wild and wacky tea bag collection*
- *count the sheep in the surrounding hills*
- *buy an organic cucumber from the local shop*
- *find en suite bathrooms you never knew existed*
- *loads of things for kids to do too*

...so don't delay — visit today.

For further details, why not visit our web site at www.beetroot.co.mars

All three of them want to look round the famous Wacky Tea Bag Collection. It costs £1.35 per person.

How much is that in total?

....
....
....

They enjoy it so much they go on the Wacky Tea Bag Ride straight afterwards. They buy two tickets each for it. It costs them £3.60 in total.

How much does it cost per go?

....
....
....

In the Sheep-Counting Contest, they each count 173 sheep every hour. How many do they count every hour between them?

....
....

Don't forget there are 3 of them. So if all of them do something, that's 3 people.

They count 1038 sheep in total. How many hours does the contest last?

Flossybot Parsons appears in Broughton Square 37 times every hour. How many times does she appear in 8 hours?

....
....

....
....

MATHS CLASSBOOK 6B

Real Life Problems

Limpet Outer Space Tours

Limpets, the Travel Agents, have started doing
tours to Saturn, Jupiter and Mars.

Paul, Noel and Joel are
their first customers.
They book themselves on the Limpet Complete Guide to the Whole Galaxy.

While passing Saturn, Noel takes 16 photos
every minute. It takes 35 minutes to pass Saturn.
How many photos does Noel take in this time?

....

....

They stop off at Jupiter to look at its fake plastic trees.
There are 232 trees, and Noel takes a photo of each.

When he gets home, he's going to share the photos equally
between his 14 friends. How many will each of them get?

....

....

....

How many will be left over?   ....

Joel discovers a new planet between Jupiter and Saturn. He wants to call it Billy.
The other 15 passengers think it's a daft name, so they think of 167 different ones.

How many names is that per person?

....

Paul meets twelve yellow aliens from Pluto, and gives
them some coins as a present. He gives them 75p each.

How much does he give in total?

....

....

Solving Problems	# Function Machines

Function machines are <u>cool</u>. No, really — they are. But only because they're <u>dead easy</u>.

One Number Goes In... and Another Comes Out

You put a number <u>in</u> a function machine, and you get a number <u>out</u>.
This is a halving machine:

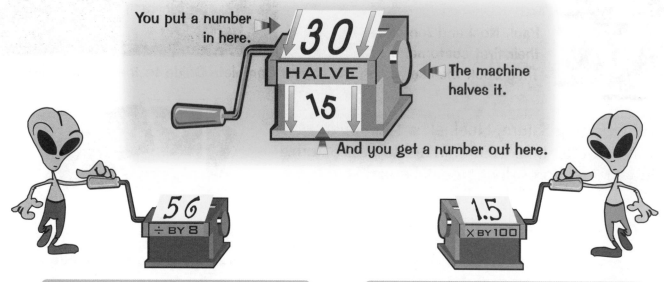

You put a number in here. → **30**

HALVE — The machine halves it.

15

↑ And you get a number out here.

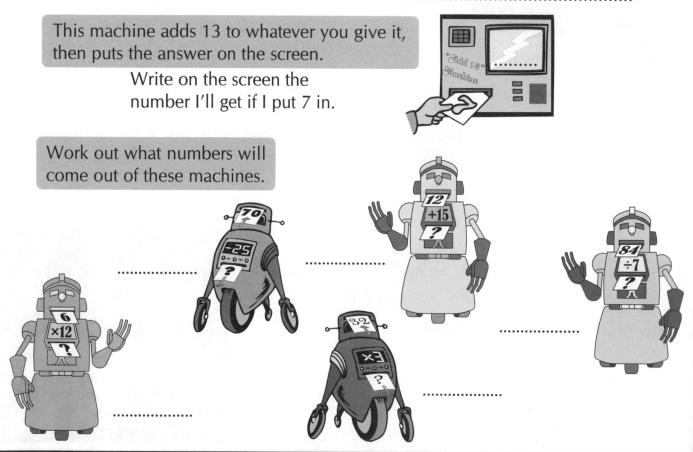

This is a "divide by 8" machine. If I put 56 in, what do I get out?

....

This is a "times by 100" machine. If I put 1.5 in, what do I get out?

....

This machine adds 13 to whatever you give it, then puts the answer on the screen.

Write on the screen the number I'll get if I put 7 in.

Work out what numbers will come out of these machines.

....

....

....

....

....

Function Machines

This is a <u>Doubling</u> Machine. I've got 100 out, but I <u>can't remember</u> what number I put in.

Help me out by working it out for me.

....

It's easy — all you need to do is halve the number I got out.

What number did I put into this machine?

....

....

What number has the alien put through this machine?

....

....

MINUS 50

130

What's in Between?

This is the bit that's not so easy.
You have to fill in what the machine is <u>doing</u> to the number put into it.
(I've given you some <u>clues</u>, to make it a bit easier.)

This machine divides 23.7 by something to squirt 2.37 out of the nozzle.

This one multiplies 12 by something to squirt 144 out of the nozzle.

What number has been subtracted from 185 to get 35?

This machine has squashed 38 into 0.38. It's divided by something, I'm sure.

....

....

What has this one divided 260 by to give out 10?

....

Real Life Problems — Calculators

You're not allowed to use calculators for <u>everything</u>, but they're handy for checking answers.

Use a Calculator to Check Your Answers

Paul, Noel and Joel go looking for fish in their garden pond. They have 19 different colours of fish, and find 31 of each colour.

How many fish do they find in total?

....

Check the answer using a calculator: .... Is your answer the same? ....

On a recent birdwatching trip, Joel sees 160 seagulls — 32 of each kind.

How many different kinds of seagull does he see?

....

Check the answer using a calculator: ....

Use your answer to the last question here...

He then sees a UFO beam up 12 of each kind of seagull.

How many is this in total? ....

How many are left? ....

Check both answers here: ....

Paul, Noel and Joel go mountain climbing every week. They climb 208 mountains each year.

How many is that each week?

Don't forget, there are 52 weeks in a year...

....

....

Check the answer using a calculator: ....

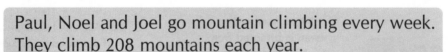

Checking with a calculator — no good in English tests...

Calculators are great for checking, but watch out in case you press the wrong button.
If your answer's different to your calculator's, do it again, don't just trust your calculator.

What are Percentages?

You've all seen the % button on your calculator — well, this is what it's all about...

"Per Cent" means "Out of 100"

This is a <u>percentage sign</u>.

30%

"30%" means "<u>thirty percent</u>"
— which is just "<u>30 out of 100</u>."

A percentage is like
a fraction with 100
on the bottom.

$$\frac{30}{100}$$

Write $\frac{28}{100}$ as a percentage. $\frac{28}{100}$ *is 28 out of 100, so it's* 28%.

Write $\frac{75}{100}$ as a percentage.   ....   Write $\frac{59}{100}$ as a percentage.   ....

Write $\frac{10}{100}$ as a percentage.   ....

Write 87% as a fraction.   ....

Swapping between fractions, decimals and percentages is <u>easy</u>.

Here are the Easy Ones You'd Better Know

These are the easy ones — if you don't know them already, then learn them <u>now</u>.

Write 50% as a fraction and a decimal.

50% is the same as $\frac{50}{100}$.

You can cancel that down to $\frac{1}{2}$.

So $\frac{1}{2}$, or 0.5, is the same as 50%.

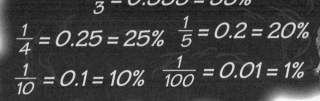

$$\frac{1}{2} = 0.5 = 50\%$$
$$\frac{1}{3} = 0.333 = 33\%$$
$$\frac{1}{4} = 0.25 = 25\% \qquad \frac{1}{5} = 0.2 = 20\%$$
$$\frac{1}{10} = 0.1 = 10\% \qquad \frac{1}{100} = 0.01 = 1\%$$

Write 75% as a fraction and a decimal.

....

....

....

Write 30% as a fraction and a decimal.

....

....

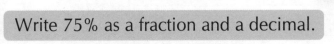

Use the conversions you already
know to work these two out.

Numbers and the Number System

Percentages, Decimals & Fractions

Percentage → Fraction → Decimal

This is <u>burningly important</u> — it makes this whole bit <u>much easier</u> once you know it.

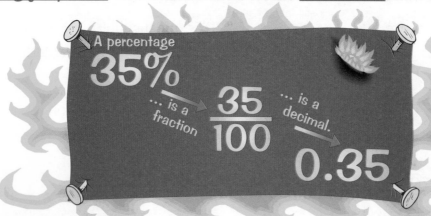

A percentage
35%
... is a fraction
$\frac{35}{100}$
... is a decimal.
0.35

Change 60% to a fraction.

<u>Remember</u> — 60% is <u>60 out of 100</u>.
And don't forget to cancel...

Change 54% to a decimal.

$54\% = \frac{54}{100}$

Put it <u>over 100</u> to make it a <u>fraction</u>.

$\frac{54}{100} = 54 \div 100 = 0.54$

<u>Divide</u> top by bottom to get a <u>decimal</u>.

Change 80% to a fraction.

Change 16% to a decimal.

Change 5% to a decimal.

Changing to a Percentage is a Bit Trickier

To <u>change to a percentage</u>, just do it all backwards.

What is $\frac{4}{5}$ as a percentage?

Turn it into a fraction with <u>100 on the bottom</u>.

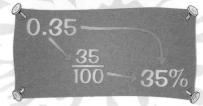

0.35
$\frac{35}{100}$ → 35%

$\frac{4}{5} = \frac{8}{10} = \frac{80}{100}$

So it's 80%.

$\frac{80}{100}$ means 80 <u>out of 100</u>, which means "<u>percent</u>."

What is 0.24 as a percentage?

What is $\frac{4}{5}$ as a percentage?

Turn it into a fraction with <u>100 on the bottom</u>.

"<u>Out of 100</u>" means "<u>percent</u>."

Exchange from US money — get 1½ p per cent...

To turn a percentage to a fraction, just stick it over 100, and cancel down. To turn a fraction to a percentage, turn it into a fraction with 100 on the bottom, and write down the top. Easy.

Finding Percentages

I always see "50% extra free" written on packets — but it never says <u>how much</u> that is...

Find Percentages by Halving and Quartering

It's time to unravel one of life's great mysteries...   Well, OK — maybe not.

50% means a half.   To find 50% of something, you *halve it* .

25% means a quarter.   To find 25% of something, you ....

I buy a pack of Froggatt's Honey-Nut Sproutflakes, which has 50% extra free.

A pack normally contains 500 g.
How much extra will I get?

Half of 500 g = ... *g*

How much will I get in total?

500 g + ... *g =* .... *g*

50% EXTRA FREE
Froggatt's Honey-Nut Sproutflakes

500 g

Find 50% of these amounts:

£36.00 ....   200 m ....   60 miles ....

Vic chops cheese. He keeps chopping until he's got 25% of the way through.

If he starts with 160 tonnes, how much does he need to chop before he can stop?

Quarter of 160 tonnes = ... *tonnes*

mmmm

My local greengrocer has a special offer on moth-eaten dresses.
They were £12.80 each, and he's now knocked 25% off.

How much money is being knocked off? ....

Ace Moldo Sweets — they're ace...

... and they're sold here.

Ace Moldo Sweets are normally in packs of 20, but there's a special offer for 25% extra free.
How many extra sweets is that?

....
How many will there be in total?

20 sweets + ... *sweets =* .... *sweets*

Numbers and the Number System

Finding Percentages

"Of" means "Times"

To find "something per cent of something else" you just turn the <u>percentage</u> into a <u>fraction</u> and <u>times</u> by it.

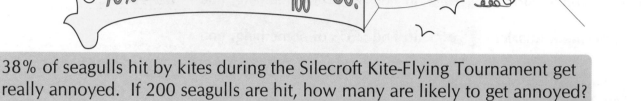

70% of 80 is the same as $\frac{70}{100} \times 80$.

38% of seagulls hit by kites during the Silecroft Kite-Flying Tournament get really annoyed. If 200 seagulls are hit, how many are likely to get annoyed?

$38\% = \frac{38}{100}$. So 38% of 200 $= \frac{38}{100} \times 200$.

Turn the percentage into a fraction, then multiply. It's easy.

$38 \div 100 \times 200 = \quad$. So $\quad$ seagulls are likely to get annoyed this year.

Work out the following percentages:

14% of 550 ferret enthusiasts: ....

90% of 1000 lemon drinks:

....

The famous band, Bewildered, agree to take an intelligence test. Their scores are shown on this chart:

Linseed	29%
Kevin	100%
Sinbad	82%
O'Dear	77%

There were 3000 questions — how many did they get right?

Linseed: .... Sinbad: ....

Kevin: .... O'Dear: ....

 *If 28% do, the rest don't.*

Out of my 50 pet dragons, 28% eat fish. What percentage don't eat fish?

$100 - 28 = \quad$ % How many dragons is this? ....

I flick 64 soggy peas at my friend Jon. 75% of them miss, but the rest land on his face, covering him in green mush.

How many peas hit Jon? ....

....

And don't just count them.

I have 20 friends, and 90% of them are witches. How many aren't?

....

Finding

Percentages can be used for <u>boring</u> things like <u>how much tax</u> you have to pay, or more <u>interesting</u> things like how much <u>bigger a chocolate bar is</u>.

For a Percentage Increase You Add it On

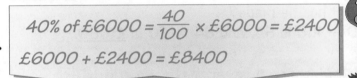

EXAMPLE: My house cost me £6 000 when I bought it. Its value has <u>increased</u> by 40%. How much is it <u>worth now</u>?

Work out 40% of £6000...

... then <u>add</u> it back on.

$$40\% \text{ of } £6000 = \frac{40}{100} \times £6000 = £2400$$

$$£6000 + £2400 = £8400$$

My mouse cost me £23 000 when I bought him. He has increased in value by 30% since then.

How much is he worth now?

Work out the percentage... ....

... then add it on. ....

I put £75 in the bank. After a year they gave me 5% interest on it. How much do I have now?

....

....

Look out for that word, "<u>interest</u>." It's the money a bank <u>adds on</u> to whatever money you've already got in your bank account.

Isn't that nice of them.

For a Percentage Decrease You Take it Away

It's exactly the <u>same idea</u> as working out a <u>percentage increase</u>. You start by working out the percentage of the total. But this time you <u>take it away</u> instead of adding it on.

This ultra-stylish Kirkby United replica shirt retails at £30. With a 20% discount, what does it cost?

....

....

Pensioners get 60% off the £20 match ticket price. How much do they pay?

....

Percentages

Finding Something Per Cent of Something Else

Finding a percentage on a <u>calculator</u> is <u>dead easy</u>.
What you do is <u>divide by 100</u>, then <u>times</u> by how many
per cent you want.

EXAMPLE: Jasper the <u>business-monkey</u> invests £5400
in Orang-U-Corp. The shares go <u>up by 20%</u>.
How much <u>profit</u> has he made?
Answer: 5400 ÷ 100 is 54, and 54 × 20 is <u>£1080</u>.

Use your calculator to answer these questions.

Jasper has to pay 33% tax on his £1080 profit.
How much tax is that?

....

Jasper puts £320 life savings in Chimps Incorporated but the stock market crashes
and he only gets 12% of his money back. How much is that?

....

Finding Percentages from Fractions

When you have to say what one number is as a <u>percentage of another</u>,
just do a simple <u>division</u> sum and <u>times by 100</u>.

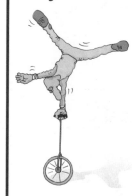

EXAMPLE: Out of 42 <u>professional one-handed unicyclists</u>,
27 were trained at the Ulverston Unicycle Academy.
What <u>percentage</u> of the unicyclists is that?
Answer: 27 ÷ 42 = 0.6428571, then times by 100 is 64.28571.
<u>Round it</u> to the nearest whole number and we get <u>64%</u>.

Use your calculator and round to the nearest whole number.

38 of the 42 professional one-handed unicyclists prefer to use
their left hand. What percentage is that?

....

A total of 70 people applied to become professional one-handed
unicyclists, but only 42 passed the test. What percentage is that?

....

Out of 219 spectators surveyed at a professional one-handed unicycling show, 149
said they preferred it to going deep sea diving. What percentage is that?

....

Mode and Range

The Mode is the Most Common

EXAMPLE: This table shows the results of the 20th annual Alien Eatathon. The aliens compete to eat the <u>most</u> Stellar Burgers.

What is the **MODE** of the number of burgers eaten?

| 3 burgers | 1 burger | 1 burger | 2 burgers | 1 burger | 2 burgers |

It's easy — the MODE is 1. Just remember — the MODE is the number which occurs MOST.

Now you try — give the mode of these numbers:

10, 15 , 5, 33, 15, 10 ,15, 7 ....   3, 7 , 16, 7, 15, 1 ,15, 7 ....

103, 18 , 29, 73, 103, 10 ,19, 2 ....   10, 19 , 24, 43, 97, 10 ,56, 87 ....

Look at this table of Aliens' heights — what is the mode of the heights?

Height in metres

This looks harder, but it's just the same — the mode is the height that occurs the most.

Number of aliens	0-1	1-2	2-3	3-4	4-5
	5	3	7	8	2

 ....

Range — From one Extreme to Another

Range is even easier —

It's the <u>difference</u> between the smallest ...

You <u>take away</u> the smallest number from the biggest number. Easy!

...and the **biggest**.

EXAMPLE:

1   3   7   18   22   34   36   42   55   61   62   63   68   71   74   83   85   92   100

100 − 1 = 99

So the range of these numbers is **99** because the difference between 1 and 100 is 99.

Your turn again — this time give the range of the numbers:

Remember: it's biggest − smallest

1, 5, 19, 25, 35 ....   2, 9 , 16, 37, 45, 61 ,70, 79 ....

4, 22, 35, 44, 57, 200 ....   1, 2, 3, 6, 9, 12, 25, 60, 61 ....

Handling Data	# *Finding Averages*

Working out the Mean *and* Median

We've already done <u>mode</u> — <u>most common</u> value,
and <u>range</u> — <u>difference</u> between highest and lowest.

Now it's time for the <u>mean</u> and the <u>median</u>.

> The <u>median</u> is the <u>middle</u> value.
>
> The <u>mean</u> is the <u>average</u> value.

EXAMPLE:

Ten <u>tennis players</u> had <u>twenty attempts</u> to see
how many times they can return the serve of
the famous big-hitter, <u>Tim Chickenman</u>.

This table shows how many times they managed it.

Fred	13	Simone	10
Gavin	9	Ashley	12
Helena	14	Ben	11
Joanna	12	Fiona	9
Alex	13	Jackie	15

The <u>median</u> is the <u>middle value</u>.
To find it, you have to put the scores <u>in order</u> and see what score is <u>in the middle</u>.

Put the numbers in order and then fill in the gaps to complete the statements.

........./ ..../ ..../ ..../ ..../ ..../ ..../ ..../ ..../ ....

There are ....*ten*.... scores, so the middle comes between

the ....*fifth*.... score and the .... score.

> If there are 2 numbers in the middle, we add them and divide by 2 to get the median.

The fifth and sixth scores are both .... So the <u>median score is</u> ....

The <u>mean</u> is the <u>average value</u>.
To find it you have to <u>add up</u> all the scores then <u>divide</u> by the number of scores.

9 + 9 + 10 + 11 + 12 + 12 + 13 + 13 + 14 + 15 = ...

There are 10 scores in total so we <u>divide the sum of the scores by 10</u>.

.... **÷ 10 =** ....

The <u>mean score is</u> ....

Finding Averages

Find the median and mean values in these sets of data.

Monday	23
Tuesday	26
Wednesday	17
Thursday	20
Friday	22
Saturday	35
Sunday	18

Alfonso puts a <u>new item</u> on the menu at his pizzeria — chocolate cookie pizza.

This table shows <u>how many times</u> Alfonso's customers order one in the first week.

Buy my Pizza — it's chocolate

Put the numbers in order ..../ ..../ ..../ ..../ ..../ ..../ ....

What is the median number of pizzas ordered per day? ....

What is the total number of pizzas? .... So what is the mean? .... ÷ 7 = ...

MILLOM MUD MUSEUM

A history of mud through the ages

This table shows <u>how many tourists</u> visited the Millom Mud Museum in <u>each month</u> last year.

January	50	July	170
February	55	August	185
March	75	September	135
April	90	October	90
May	100	November	60
June	145	December	45

Put the numbers in order:

........./ ..../ ..../ ..../ ..../ ..../ ..../ ..../ ..../ ..../ ..../ ....

What was the median number of visitors per month? ....

What was the total number of visitors throughout the year? ....

What number do you have to divide by to find the mean number for a month? ....

So what is the mean? .... ÷ .... = ...

Add them up then divide — now that's a mean trick...

Don't get the 3 "<u>M</u>"s mixed up. <u>M</u>edian is the <u>middle</u> value, <u>M</u>ode is the <u>most</u>, and mean is the average (think "average is mean because you have to calculate it.")

Line Graphs

Drawing a Line Graph from a Table

Every year the islanders of Noonos drag their island a
few miles to the south to make their island <u>warmer</u>.

This table shows how their <u>average</u>
yearly temperature has increased.

1990	13 °C	1995	23 °C
1991	15 °C	1996	24 °C
1992	16 °C	1997	26 °C
1993	18 °C	1998	28 °C
1994	22 °C	1999	29 °C

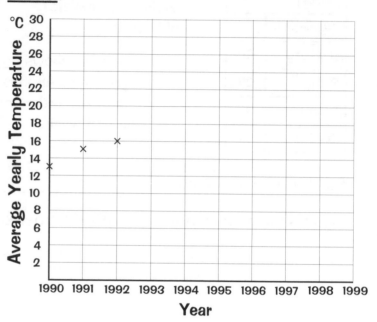

I've marked the first three points on the graph for you.

Complete the line graph above showing this data.

As Noonos was dragged into a warmer climate, the
amount of rain that fell each year started to get <u>lower</u>.

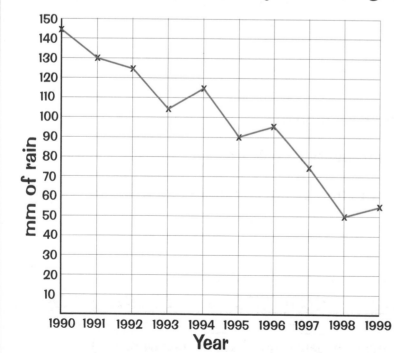

Use the line graph to fill in
the table showing how many
mm of rain fell each year.

1990	145 mm	1995	
1991	130 mm	1996	
1992	125 mm	1997	
1993		1998	
1994		1999	

Line Graphs

Reading Information from Line Graphs

The line on this graph lets you <u>convert</u> <u>miles</u> to <u>kilometres</u> and <u>kilometres</u> to <u>miles</u>.

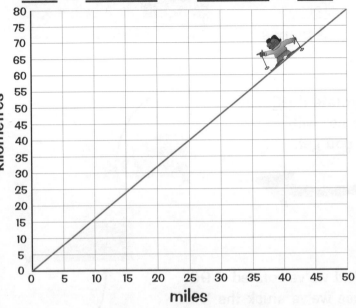

Ivory Coast ~~30 m~~ 48 km

Trunkton 25 m

Nellie is changing the road sign from miles to kilometres.

Look at the line graph — how many kilometres is it to Trunkton?

How many miles is 23 km? ....

....

How many km is 44 miles? ....

How many miles is 57 km? ....

How many km is 17 miles? ....

It's impossible to get an <u>exact answer</u> to all these questions using these graphs — so make the <u>best guess</u> you can.

This graph shows the <u>exchange rate</u> between pounds and schmollars, the currency on the island of Noonos.

You can use it to <u>convert</u> pounds to schmollars and back again.

How many schmollars would you get for £2.40? ....

How many pounds is 94 schmollars worth? ....

How many schmollars does £8.75 buy? ....

How many pounds is 136 schmollars worth? ....

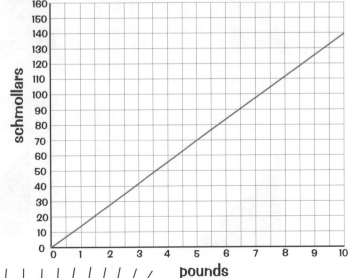

These are easy — if it's in pounds just read off the scmollars, if it's in schmollars then read off the pounds.

Measures, Shape and Space

Rotation

Remember you can rotate shapes by <u>drawing</u> them on tracing paper, putting a <u>pencil</u> on a point to hold it down, and <u>swizzling</u> the paper around.

Rotating Shapes through 90°

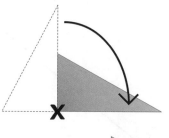
<u>90°</u> is a <u>quarter turn</u>
<u>180°</u> is a <u>half turn</u>

If you rotate shapes around <u>different</u> <u>corners</u>, you get shapes in <u>different places</u>.

Here's a shape. If you rotate it <u>90°</u> <u>clockwise</u> around the corner with the X on it, this is what you get.

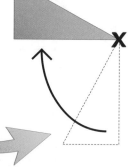

This is the <u>same shape</u>. And we've rotated it 90° clockwise too. But because we've stuck the X on a <u>different corner</u>, the result is different.

Draw what you get when you rotate these shapes 90° clockwise around the corner with the X.

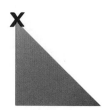

I'm not so keen on rotations any more.

Rotation

Rotating Shapes through 180°

Rotate these shapes through 180°. I've done the first one for you.

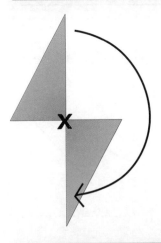  

Rotate these shapes and give their coordinates.

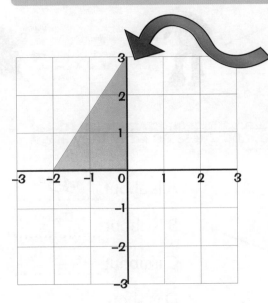

This shape has these co-ordinates:

(0,0)   (–2, 0)   (0,3)

Draw in what happens when you rotate the shape 90° clockwise around the corner at (0,0).

What are the coordinates of the new shape?

....

Now draw in what happens when you rotate the original shape by 180°, again around (0,0).

What are the coordinates of the new shape?

....

The green shape has these coordinates:

(0,0)   (3, 0)   (3,3)

Draw in what happens when you rotate the shape 90° clockwise around the corner at (0,0).

What are the coordinates of the new shape?

....

Now draw in what happens when you rotate the original shape by 180°, again around (0,0).

What are the coordinates of the new shape?

....

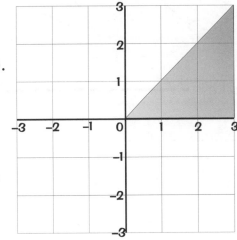

Measures, Shape and Space	Angles

Acute and Obtuse Angles

> An __acute__ angle is __less than 90°__.

> An __obtuse__ angle is __between 90° and 180°__.

Are these angles acute or obtuse? Write down the right word under each angle.

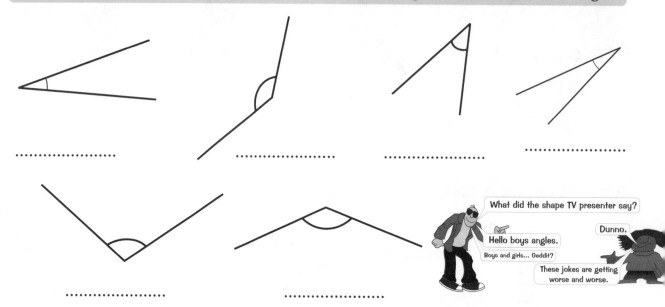

....

....

What did the shape TV presenter say?

Hello boys angles.

Boys and girls... Geddit?

Dunno.

These jokes are getting worse and worse.

Put these angles in order, from smallest to biggest, and guess how big they are.

A   B   C

D   E   F

A is about ...... *45°* ......

B is about ....

C is about ....

D is about ....

E is about ....

F is about ....

Smallest ⟶ Biggest

.........,' ....,' ....,' ....,' ....,' ....

Don't measure them yet — have a __guess__ first and see if you can get them right to the nearest 5°.

Angles ...., ... and .... are acute.

Angles ...., ... and .... are obtuse.

Angles

Measure and Draw Acute and Obtuse Angles

Use a protractor to measure these angles.

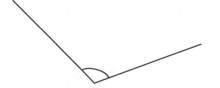

This angle measures ....

Is it acute or obtuse? ....

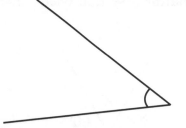

This angle measures ....

Is it acute or obtuse? ....

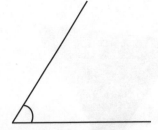

This angle measures ....

Is it acute or obtuse? ....

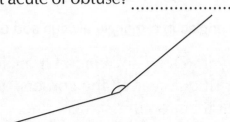

This angle measures ....

Is it acute or obtuse? ....

This angle measures ....

Is it acute or obtuse? ....

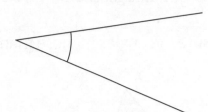

This angle measures ....

Is it acute or obtuse? ....

Use a protractor to draw an angle of 75°.

Now draw an angle of 138°.

Hmm, don't like this one.
Think I'll go for the pro-tractor.

Tractor for
the Amateur

Tractor for
the Pro

Measures, Shape and Space	# Angles of a Triangle

The Angles in a _Straight Line_ Add Up to _180°_

No matter <u>how</u> you divide them up, the angles in a straight line <u>always</u> add up to 180°.

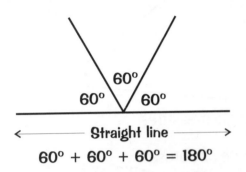

<---- Straight line ---->

60° + 60° + 60° = 180°

Use your <u>protractor</u> to check these angles are right.

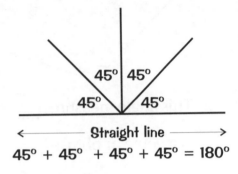

<---- Straight line ---->

45° + 45° + 45° + 45° = 180°

The angles in a <u>triangle</u> always add up to 180°, too.

Try it. Draw any kind of triangle, cut it out, tear off the corners, and put them on this straight line.

Like this.

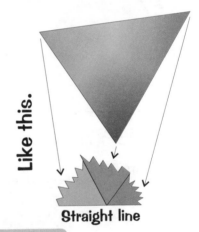

Straight line

<---- Straight line ---->

Measure the angles in these triangles and add them up.

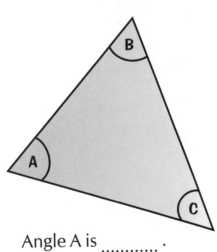

Angle A is ....

Angle B is ....

Angle C is ....

They add up to ....

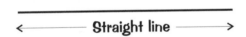

Angle A is .... Angle B is ....

Angle C is .... They add up to ....

Now draw your own triangle and add up the angles.

Angles of a Triangle

Work Out the Third Angle in a Triangle

You know that the three angles in a triangle <u>always</u> add up to 180°.
This means that you can work out what the <u>third angle</u> is if you know the <u>other two</u>.
You don't need to use a protractor!

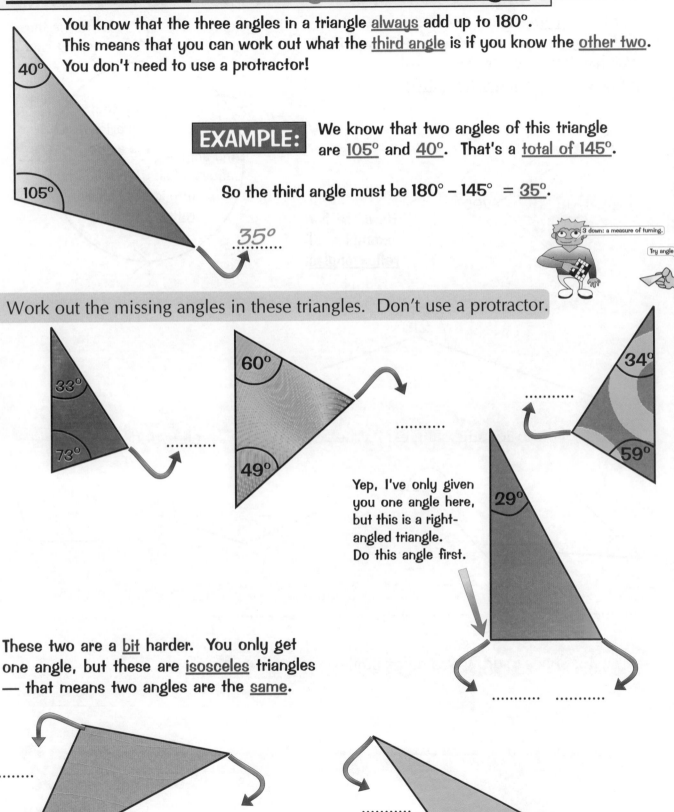

EXAMPLE: We know that two angles of this triangle are <u>105°</u> and <u>40°</u>. That's a <u>total of 145°</u>.

So the third angle must be 180° – 145° = <u>35°</u>.

_35°_

3 down: a measure of turning.

Try angle

Work out the missing angles in these triangles. Don't use a protractor.

Yep, I've only given you one angle here, but this is a right-angled triangle.
Do this angle first.

These two are a <u>bit</u> harder. You only get one angle, but these are <u>isosceles</u> triangles — that means two angles are the <u>same</u>.

You can tell which angles are the same from the picture, and work it out from that.

Reflex Angles

Reflex Angles are Bigger Than 180°

You know <u>acute</u> angles are less than 90°.
And <u>obtuse</u> angles are between 90° and 180°.
Well here's a new one for you —
<u>reflex</u> angles are <u>more than 180°</u>.

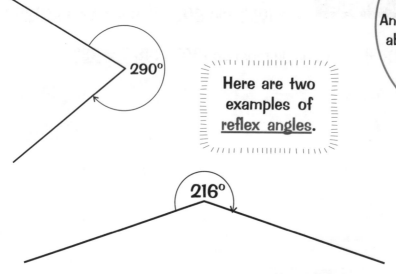

If this is the starting line...

Up to a quarter turn is <u>acute</u>.

And anything above a half turn is <u>reflex</u>. From quarter to half turn is <u>obtuse</u>.

90°

180°

290°

Here are two examples of <u>reflex angles</u>.

216°

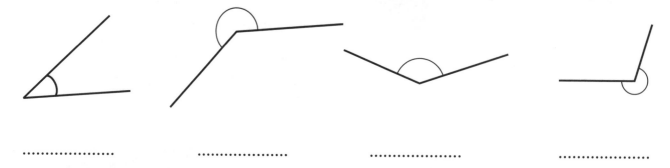

Which of these are reflex angles? Write acute, obtuse or reflex under each angle.

....

Use this space to draw two reflex angles of your own.

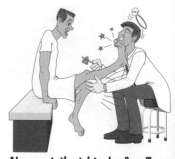

No, not that kind of reflex.

Angles at a Point

Angles around a Point Add Up to 360°

You know that a quarter turn is 90°, and a half turn is 180°.
So if you turn the whole way round a point, it's 360°.

That means if you're told what one angle at a point is,
you can work out the other angle by taking it away from 360°.

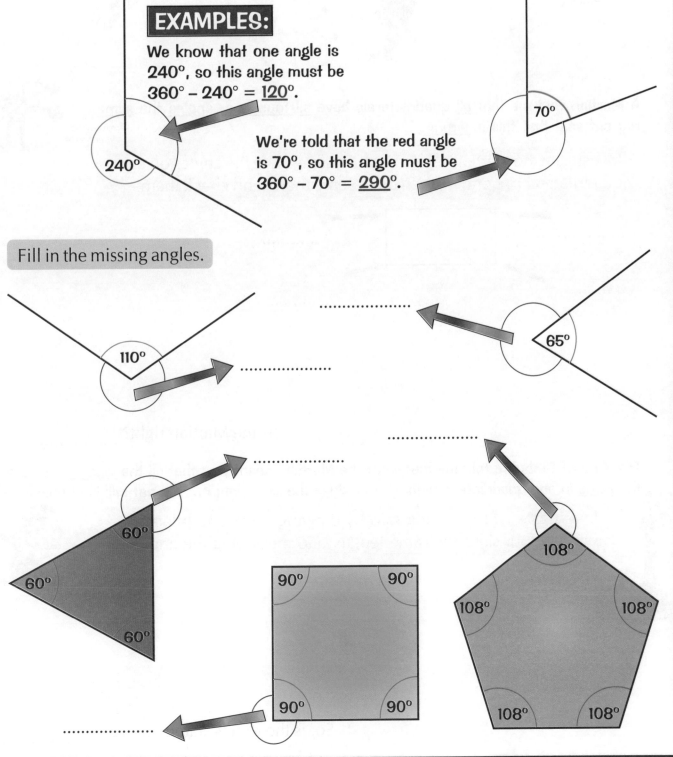

EXAMPLES:

We know that one angle is
240°, so this angle must be
360° – 240° = 120°.

240°

We're told that the red angle
is 70°, so this angle must be
360° – 70° = 290°.

70°

Fill in the missing angles.

110°

....

....

65°

60°

....

60°

60°

60°

....

90° 90°

90° 90°

....

108°

108° 108°

108° 108°

....

Reasoning About Shapes

Investigating Inner Angles

Inner angle means the angle INSIDE the shape.
So all these coloured angles are inner angles.

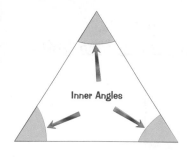

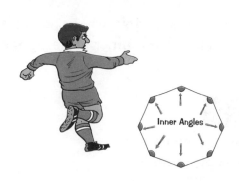

A Martian told me that <u>all</u> quadrilaterals have <u>all four inner angles</u> the <u>same</u>.
My cat said that this is <u>wrong</u>.

A talking cat?
That's ridiculous.

Investigate the Martian's statement. First measure the angles on the
quadrilateral I've drawn, then draw some more, and check them.

....

....

Is the Martian right? ....

The King of Timbuktu told me that what the Martian meant was that <u>all</u> the <u>inner angles</u> are
the <u>same</u> in any quadrilateral with <u>all four sides</u> the <u>same length</u>. My cat still isn't convinced.

Investigate what the King said by drawing some quadrilaterals
with all four sides the same length, and measuring the angles.

So, is the King's statement right? ....

Reasoning About Shapes

More about Inner Angles

Yesterday I found this piece of paper:

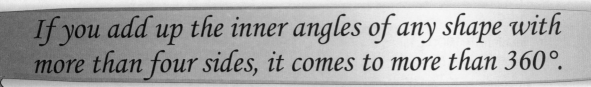

If you add up the inner angles of any shape with more than four sides, it comes to more than 360°.

Test the statement on the paper by measuring the angles in these shapes and adding them up.

   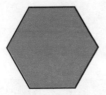   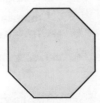

....

....

Sometimes, a statement is <u>true</u> for shapes with all their sides the <u>same length</u>, but <u>isn't true</u> for other shapes.

Test the statement on the paper by drawing some shapes with different length sides, and measuring the angles.

Do you think the statement on the paper is true? ....

It's an investigation — call Sherlock Holmes...

You <u>don't</u> need to <u>remember all the details</u> about angles and shapes — the <u>important</u> thing is <u>investigating the statements</u>, by trying them out and seeing if they work.

Measures, Shape and Space	# Units of Time

Time comes in Lots of Different Units

You already know about <u>minutes</u>, <u>seconds</u>, <u>days</u>, <u>weeks</u> and stuff like that.
They're all ways of measuring <u>time</u>. But do you remember <u>all</u> of this lot?

1 millennium = 1000 years
1 century = 100 years
1 decade = 10 years
1 year = 12 months or 52 weeks or 365 days
1 leap year = 366 days
1 week = 7 days
1 day = 24 hours
1 hour = 60 minutes
1 minute = 60 seconds

Use reasonable units
You wouldn't time someone in a race in days, and you wouldn't measure the time until the school holidays in seconds. That would be daft.

I'm a leap year

If you know that lot, and you can do easy sums, these should be a doddle.

Howard the spaceman flew right around the galaxy in 1 millennium and 3 decades.

How long did it take in years? ....

Mike Cobbler drove round the Elburton racing track in 3 minutes and 34 seconds.

How much is that in seconds? ....

Miss I B Bright took 1 millennium, 3 centuries, 4 decades and 7 years to do her maths test.

How long is that in years? ....

Months have Different Numbers of Days

This <u>rhyme</u> will help you to remember how many <u>days</u> there are in each <u>month</u>.

*30 days have September, April, June and November.
All the rest have 31, Except for February alone,
which has 28 days clear and 29 in each leap year.*

How many days in September? .... How about October? ....

How many days in March? .... And in April? .... What about May? ....

How many days in February in a leap year? .... And in every other year? ....

Problems Involving Time

Use your knowledge of time units to answer these questions.

Chef Albert's speciality is a giant vegetarian nut roast. The <u>amount of time</u> it has to be cooked depends on how heavy it is. For every kg of nut roast, it needs <u>45 minutes</u> in the oven.

How long would a 3 kg roast need to cook?

.... hours .... mins

How about a 5 kg roast?

.... hours .... mins

Albert decides to buy a huge new cooker so he can cook even <u>bigger</u> nut roasts. He agrees to pay the cooker company <u>£20 a month</u> for the next <u>30 months</u>.

Will he still be paying in two years' time? .... How about after three years? ....

The cooker comes with a guarantee that lasts for two decades.

If the cooker breaks down after 17 years, will it be covered by the guarantee? ....

How about if it breaks down after 23 years? ....

Albert employs Derek to do all his washing up. Derek can wash up <u>one plate</u> every <u>12 seconds</u>.

How many plates can Derek wash up in ten minutes? ....

How long would it take him to wash up 125 plates? ....

Derek started his job on the 1st of February. It's not a leap year. He's now been in his job for 90 days. So what month must it be? ....

Derek gets a bonus after he's been in his job for 14 weeks. If he's been there 90 days already, in how many days time will Derek get his bonus? ....

Measures, Shape and Space

Time Zones

Different Times Around the World

Britain is here — and the sun is shining on Britain, so it must be daytime.

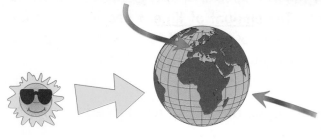

But Australia is hidden round the back here.
You can't see it, and neither can the sun.
While it's light in Britain, it's dark in Australia.

Strewth, mate, I can't see well
enough to light the barbie.

Think what would happen if everyone did the same thing at the same time everywhere in the world. Down in Australia they'd have to eat their lunch in the middle of the night.

That would be a bit daft. So instead we have different time zones around the world.

Those wavy red lines
divide up the time zones.

Whew, looks like a complicated map to me. But don't worry, you don't need to know too much about it, as long as you get the general idea.

Brisbane in Australia is ten time zones to the right of Britain.
That means the time is always ten hours later in Brisbane than it is in London.
So when it's lunchtime in London, it's just about time to go to bed in Brisbane.

New York in America is five time zones to the left of Britain.
So it's always five hours earlier in New York than it is in Britain.
When it's lunchtime in Britain and bedtime in Brisbane, it's only just time to get up in New York

It's 1:00 pm in Britain. What time is it in Brisbane? ....

It's 1:00 pm in Britain. What time is it in New York? ....

It's 8:45 am in Britain. What time is it in Brisbane? ....

It's 8:45 am in Britain. What time is it in New York? ....

Time Zones

In Britain it's the same time everywhere. But bigger countries span several time zones.

There are four time zones in America. It gets one hour later each time zone you go to the right.

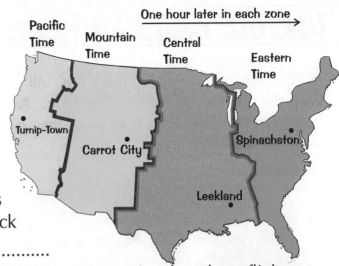

One hour later in each zone →

Pacific Time
Mountain Time
Central Time
Eastern Time

Turnip-Town
Carrot City
Spinachston
Leekland

Look at the map to find the answers.

Daisy, who lives in Turnip-Town, phones her friend Stacey in Leekland. Daisy's clock says 6.30 pm. What does Stacey's say? ....

A plane leaves Spinachston at 8.15 am to fly to Carrot City. It's a three-hour flight. What time do the clocks in Carrot City say on arrival? ....

The Super Bowl

The Super Bowl kicks off in Turnip-Town at 1.30 pm. What time should you turn the TV on in Spinachston to watch it ? ....

Jim-Bob gets up at 6 am in Carrot City. He has promised to call his cousin Mary in Leekland at 9 am Leekland time. How long does he have to wait? ....

Different Times *During the Year*

In Britain we put our clocks forward an hour at the start of summer, then turn them back again after summer. It's all so we can enjoy the sun (if there is any).
It gets light earlier in winter, and dark later in summer.

> When the clock's been put forward we call it British Summer Time.
> The rest of the time it's Greenwich Mean Time.

It's autumn. It gets dark at 6 pm. Later tonight, British Summer Time ends and Greenwich Mean Time begins.

What time will it get dark tomorrow? ....

It's spring. It gets light at 5 am. British Summer Time is about to begin, so the clocks go forward an hour.

What time will it get light tomorrow? ....

It's spring, and British Summer Time will begin tonight. It's 7pm now.

What time will it be in 12 hours? ....

GREENWICH is a place near London, and MEAN means average. It's nothing to do with mean, green witches.

Calculations

Mental Calculations

Making Decimals up to the _Nearest Whole_

Sometimes you have to make a number up to the <u>next whole number</u>.
You have to work out what to <u>add on</u> to make the number whole.

EXAMPLE: I have 3.7 litres of sprout milkshake, but I
need 4 litres. How much more do I need?

3.7 + 0.3 = 4, so I need another 0.3 litres.

That's not a whole
— this is a hole.

It's easier if you think of 4 litres as 4.0.

Now see if you can work out these ones:

Bob's weightlifting bar weighs 6.53 kg. He wants it to be a whole number.
How much must he add to the bar to make it up to 7 kg?

....

....

This one's a bit harder. Try doing it in <u>2 steps</u>. First make <u>6.53 up to 6.6</u>,
then make <u>6.6 up to 7</u>. You'll get 2 numbers, which you just <u>add together</u>.

Sally has scored 54.32 points in the national Jelly-Flop Finals.
How much does she need to reach 55 points?

....

....

Now have a go at these quick ones. See how many of them you can do in your head...

3.72 + ... = 4   2.44 + ... = 3   6.79 + ... = 7

.... + 9.99 = 10   .... + 0.65 = 1   .... + 4.32 = 5

Hole numbers? You get them on golf courses...

Always look for ways to make sums easier — like splitting these ones up into 2 parts.
The other thing is — check you've put your decimal point in. If you don't, it will be wrong.

Mental Calculations

Decimals don't really make sums harder — you work them out the <u>same way</u>.
The only difference is you have to put the <u>decimal point</u> in your answer.

Adding and Subtracting *Decimals*

You can often split simple sums into 2 bits. Work out the tenths
and hundredths <u>separately</u>, then put the answers together.

EXAMPLE:

Sarah entered a mole-vaulting competition.
She scored 0.45 points with her first vault, but only
0.23 with her second. What did she score in total?

> 0.45 is **4** tenths and **5** hundredths
> 0.23 is **2** tenths and **3** hundredths

Try adding the tenths and hundredths separately:

> **4** tenths + **2** tenths = <u>6 tenths</u>
> **5** hundredths + **3** hundredths = <u>8 hundredths</u>

So Sarah scored 6 tenths and 8 hundredths, which is just 0.68.

Now see if you can do these in the same way:

Jerry and Steve are practising for the World
Windsurfing Contest. Jerry has raised 0.15p in
sponsorship, but Steve has raised 0.24p. How
much money have they raised altogether?

Add up the tenths first: ....

Now add up the hundredths: ....

So they have raised .... in sponsorship altogether.

Mary had 0.78 kg of custard powder, but she lost 0.35 kg of it
when her pocket leaked. How much does she have now?

....

Watch out!
This one's a
subtraction —
not an addition.

....

Finally, have a go at these. See if you can do them in your head...

0.63 + 0.04 = ...   0.66 – 0.12 = ...   0.37 – 0.26 = ...

0.49 + 0.3 = ...   0.44 – 0.2 = ...   0.9 + 0.01 = ...

0.68 + 0.11 = ...   0.19 – 0.11 = ...   0.98 – 0.36 = ...

| Calculations | **_Adding Decimals_** |

Add Decimals the Same Way as Whole Numbers

You can <u>add decimals</u> the same way you add <u>big numbers</u> — put them in <u>columns</u>.

EXAMPLE: What is <u>5421.25 + 2717.4</u>?

Line up the <u>decimal point</u>...

... put them into <u>columns</u>...

... then <u>do the sum</u>.

Always line up the decimal point first.

Whoops — no number. Better add a nought.

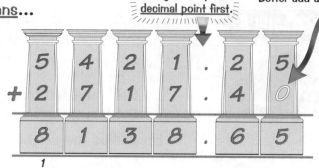

This stuff's <u>no harder</u> than adding <u>small numbers</u>. You've just got a few <u>more columns</u> to add up.

So, the answer is <u>8138.65</u>.

Now have a go at these. They're already in columns, so you just have to add them.

```
   232.14          783.04          1656.92
 +256.25         +  56.13         +310.35
 ─────────       ─────────        ─────────
   488.39
```

Ha ha, these aren't in columns — make sure you do that bit first.

1354.2 + 23.03   327.49 + 205.2   3005.02 + 252   1212.40 + 422.06

```
+_____         +_____         +_____         +_____
_____          _____          _____          _____
```

This one's only got words and some measurements, so watch out...

Bill has won Lincoln's Largest Lemon competition three years in a row. His entry for this year is still growing. It weighed 1.57 kg last week, but has grown 30 g more this week. How heavy is the lemon now?

1 kg = 1000 g, so 0.1 kg = 100 g.

Subtracting Decimals

Subtract Decimals *Using* Columns *Too*

Now you've got the hang of adding decimals, subtracting is going to be a doddle.
It's the same thing — line up the decimal point, then put the numbers in columns.

EXAMPLE: What is 6375.89 – 4624.32?

Line up the decimal point...

... put them in columns...

... smaller number underneath...

... and subtract as normal.

```
  5
  6 ¹3 7 5 . 8 9
- 4  6 2 4 . 3 2
  1  7 5 1 . 5 7
```

So the answer's 1751.57.

See, it's easy peasy.
You've just got to keep practising.
Which is lucky, because...

Here's some practice for you to do. Don't say I never give you anything.

```
  476.64        783.04        1656.92
-  52.32      -  56.13      -  310.35
  424.32
```

No columns — you've got to do that bit yourself.

515.69 – 23.12   468.75 – 138.33   1789.5 – 321.4   9413.65 – 2161.71

Bill is entering his lemon in Lincoln's Largest Lemon competition.
On the night before the competition it weighs 5.6 kg — but during the night,
a grub eats a big chunk out of it, so in the morning it only weighs 3.9 kg.

What was the weight of the chunk the grub ate?

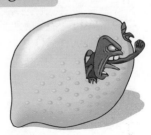

Rows of sums — it's like Column-ation Street...

Remember the four steps, and you'll find these easy: 1) line up the decimal point,
2) put the numbers in columns, 3) smaller one underneath, 4) do the sum as normal.

Numbers and the Number System

Prime Numbers

Prime Numbers can't be Divided by Anything

A <u>prime number</u> is a number that DOES NOT DIVIDE BY ANYTHING.
This means they are <u>not in any times tables</u>.
Here are the first few:

1 <u>isn't</u> a prime. It just isn't.

| 2 | 3 | 5 | 7 | 11 | 13 | 17 | 19 | 23 | 29 | 31 . . . |

Here's a good way of <u>checking</u> if a number is a prime number or not:

1) First of all, try <u>dividing it by 2</u>. If you don't get a remainder, STOP — your number is <u>not</u> a prime.
2) Then try <u>dividing it by 3</u>. If you don't get a remainder, STOP — your number is <u>not</u> a prime.
3) Then try <u>dividing it by 4</u>. If you don't get a remainder...... Get the idea?

When you get to dividing by <u>half of the number</u>, you can stop.
If you've got a remainder <u>each time</u>, then your number is a <u>prime</u>.

In fact, it's even easier. You don't have to divide by <u>everything</u> up to half of your number — just by the <u>prime numbers</u>.

EXAMPLE:

I'm going to try it out on **29**.

17 would be next, but it's <u>more than half</u> of **29**, so we can stop. There was a remainder each time, so <u>29 is a prime</u>!

29 ÷ 2 = 14 rem 1
29 ÷ 3 = 9 rem 2
29 ÷ 5 = 5 rem 4
29 ÷ 7 = 4 rem 1
29 ÷ 11 = 2 rem 7
29 ÷ 13 = 2 rem 3

If a number ends in an even number or in a 5, then it's <u>not prime</u> unless the number itself is 2 or 5.

Your turn. Work out if these are primes or not.

13 *13 ÷ 2 = 7 rem 1, 13 ÷ 3 = 6 rem 1, 13 ÷ 5 = 2 rem 2*

So it doesn't divide by anything. So 13 is a prime.

40 ....

....

41 ....

....

Some more quick ones — put a ring around the primes.

13   25   36   42   2   1   17   29   32   60

Factors and Dividing

You can _Divide_ a Number _Exactly_ by its _Factors_

The _factors_ of a number are the numbers it's divisible by.

EXAMPLE: Find all the factors of 14.

$14 \div 1 = 14$ so 1 is a factor. $14 \div 2 = 7$ so 2 is a factor.
$14 \div 3 = 4$ rem 2   so 3 is **NOT** a factor. $14 \div 4 = 3$ rem 2   so 4 is **NOT** a factor.
$14 \div 5 = 2$ rem 4   so 5 is **NOT** a factor. $14 \div 6 = 2$ rem 2   so 6 is **NOT** a factor.
$14 \div 7 = 2$ so 7 is a factor.

We _don't_ need to try any more numbers because 7 is half of 14.
So the _only_ number bigger than 7 which can divide into 14 is 14.
So the _factors of 14_ are 1, 2, 7 and 14.

I think I'm lost... I'm supposed to be in a Science book.

Write down the factors of the following numbers.

20 ....

15 ....

36 ....

80 ....

Prime Factors — _Factorise the Factors_

Prime factors are factors that are _prime numbers_.
To find them, you just find the _factors_, and then see if you can _factorise_ them.

EXAMPLE: Find the prime factors of 100.

$$100 = 2 \times 50$$
But $50 = 2 \times 25$, so $100 = 2 \times 2 \times 25$
But $25 = 5 \times 5$, so $100 = 2 \times 2 \times 5 \times 5$
2 and 5 are both _prime numbers_, so
2, 2, 5 and 5 are the prime factors of 100.

Factorise just means find the factors of a number and write them down like this:
$2 \times 7 = 14$

Break these numbers into their prime factors.

60 ....

84 ....

92 ....

The factor the matter is they're easy questions...

There you go, a page all about factors and prime factors. Just what you always wanted.
This is pretty easy — if you remember what these words mean. So make sure you do.

Using Formulas to Solve Problems

Using Formulas — Letters instead of Numbers

Formulas are a way of using <u>letters</u> to stand for <u>numbers</u>, instead of using the numbers themselves. It might look a bit confusing at first — but they can make life a lot <u>easier</u>.

A <u>formula is like a recipe</u>, telling you what to do to numbers.

NUMBERS

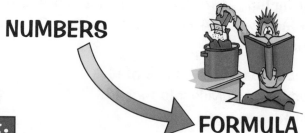

FORMULA

ANSWER

EXAMPLE:

Billy Bonker has a chocolate factory where he makes his famous <u>Ever-Lasting-Gob-Starter</u>. He sells them at <u>99p</u> each.

If we put <u>n</u> for the <u>number</u> of sweets sold, and <u>c</u> for the <u>cost</u> of that many sweets (in pence), then we can write:

$$c = 99 \times n$$

If someone buys <u>100</u> sweets, then n is <u>100</u>.
Now we can work out <u>c</u>, the <u>total cost</u>:
c = 99 × n = 99 × 100 = 9900.
So Billy was paid 9900p, which is £99.

That's all a formula is, like a normal sum but with <u>letters</u> standing in for <u>numbers</u>.

Use the formula above to solve these problems.

If Billy sells 500 sweets, how much money will he get? ....

If I buy two of his sweets, how much will it cost me? ....

If I buy 238 of his sweets, how much will it cost me? ....

Another sweet making company (Sludge's Sweets) make <u>mud-flavoured chocolate mice</u>. They cost <u>55p</u> each.

Write a formula for the total cost of n sweets, if the total cost is c.

....

My cat buys 6 of Sludge's chocolate mice. How much does it cost him?

....

Using Formulas to Solve Problems

More Formulas

Try these to see how using formulas can make your life easier.

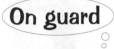

Farmer Fields runs a fencing company called Fields' Field Fencing. He has to work out how many posts he needs for each field.

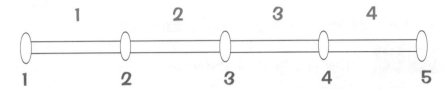

He needs a post on the left of each length and then one extra on the right. That's 1 more <u>post (in blue)</u> than the number of <u>lengths of fence (in red)</u>.

Write a formula to work out the <u>number of posts (p)</u> from the number of <u>lengths of fence (f)</u> : $p =$ ....

Use your formula to see how many posts he needs for a field with 20 lengths of fence ....

A talking goat? Fency that.

He also needs to work out the <u>perimeter</u> (<u>length</u> around the edge) of the fields.

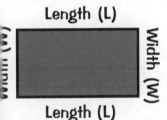

Length (L)
Width (W)
Length (L)

The length all the way round is <u>2 lengths</u> and <u>2 widths</u>.

Write a formula for working out the perimeter (P) of the rectangle.
$P =$ ....

Now use your formulas to answer these questions.

How many fence posts does Farmer Fields need for 120 lengths of fence?

....

What is the perimeter (P) of a field of length (L) 20 m and width (W) 5 m?

....

Maths for racing cars — that's Formula 1...

It's the same as normal sums but we use letters to stand in for numbers, so we've got a recipe to give us the answer. Stick in the values for the letters and you've got a sum. Easy.

Solving Problems	# Investigating General Statements

Finding a Match for a Statement

General statements are dead important in maths because they <u>tell you things which are always true</u>.

> I'm GENERAL STATEMENT and I'm VERY IMPORTANT.

You can check they aren't wrong by finding <u>examples</u>.

EXAMPLE: This is a general statement :

> If you add three <u>consecutive</u> numbers, the total will be three times the middle number.

<u>Consecutive</u> numbers are one after the other, like 7, 8 and 9 — or like 1, 2 and 3...

To check this, you could <u>pick</u> three <u>consecutive</u> numbers and try it. Let's try 7, 8 and 9...

$7 + 8 + 9 = \underline{24}$
The <u>middle number</u> is 8, and 3×8 is <u>24</u>.

So the sum of these numbers is 3 times the middle number.
Our example <u>agrees</u> with the statement, so the statement <u>could be right</u>.

Think of examples to match these general statements.

If you times by 25, that's the same as multiplying by 100 and dividing by 4.

....

Think about drawing an example and measuring the angles.

All the angles in a triangle add up to 180 degrees.

....

Any number that divides exactly by 6 is even.

....

It doesn't matter which way round you multiply 2 numbers, the answer will be the same.

....

The end is nigh — apart from the index...

Examples are great. Examples that match a general statement help to check it's right. Plus, it helps check you know what the statement really means. A cracking subject for the last page.

Answers: Pages 1–11

Page 1 — Imperial and Metric Units

"From imperial to metric...."
approximately: **7.5 km**, **2 litres**, **300 g**,

"Metric units in imperial..."
approximately: **18 pints**, **30 pounds**, **4 inches**,
200 inches / 16 feet / 5½ yards.

"Estimate each measurement...":
Any sensible estimate, for example:
A rat: **0.5 kg or about a pound**,
milk in a jug: **0.25 litres or half a pint**,
a badger: **35 cm or 15 inches**,
Tyrannosaurus Rex: **about 5 metres / 5 yards / 15 feet**.

Page 2 — Perimeters

"Perimeters...."
The grinning yellow shape is **32 cm**,
Tony's desk: **40 cm** and **no** it's not big enough.
The odd shaped pig is **42 cm**.

Page 3 — Perimeters

"Perimeters.."
28 cm, **96 cm**, **480 cm**

Page 4 — Areas

"Walter's cake tins..."
600 cm², 400 cm², 350 cm².
The tin with the stars on it.

"Area of each bit.."
Little rectangle = 1 cm × **2 cm** = **2 cm²**
Big rectangle = 3 cm × 3 cm = **9 cm²**
Total Area = **2 cm²** + **9 cm²** = **11 cm²**

"Piece of metal.."
Left rectangle = 3 m × 5 m = **15 m²**
Right rectangle = 4 m × 2 m = **8 m²**
Total area = 15 m² + 8 m² = **23 m²**

Page 5 — Areas

"Missing side lengths..."
2 m, **9 cm**, **7 m**, **5 cm**,
Height = 5 m, **Length = 8 m**

"Areas of triangles..."
9 cm², **45 m²**, **10 cm²**

Page 6 — Measurements

"Alfredo's car is..."
5000 metres from home. He has **1 km** left to walk.

"Measurement sums..."
370 cm or 3.7 m, **6 inches**, **8 kg or 8000 g**,
6453 ml or 6.453 l, **500 m or 0.5 km**.

"Alfredo can walk..." **4 km** each day in his new shoes.

"Larger amount of each pair.."
1 kg, **3000 m**, **1 litre**, **41 pints**.

Page 7 — Measurements

"Suggest how to measure..."
Weigh 100 paper clips, then divide by 100.
Answer: **0.39 g**
**Put 10 pennies on top of each other, measure the
height and divide by 10**.
Answer: **1.7 mm**
Measure a pad of 50 sheets and divide by 50.
Answer: **0.1 mm** (this varies a fair bit depending on the
paper).

"Rat and Toad Pie..."
2250 ml of water, **90 grams** of toad,
900 grams of rat,
360 grams of flour, **4** pigeon eggs and **2** drops of sickly
sauce.

Page 8 — Graphs, Charts and Tables

"Kilos of chocolate eaten..."
Derek ate the most, he ate **90 kg**, Brian ate **45 kg**.

"Escaped zoo animals..."
Keiran saw **43** animals, he saw **8** leopards, **12** more
giant rats were seen than orangutangs.

Page 9 — Graphs, Charts and Tables

"Giant Toad of Furness..."
The toad ate most cows on **Wednesday**.
He ate **21** in total.

"Cheese mountains ..."

CHEESE	TALLY	FREQUENCY
Stilton	ⵏ ⵏ ⵏ ⵏ I	21
Cheddar	ⵏ ⵏ II	12
Camembert	ⵏ ⵏ ⵏ I	16
Garlic Roule	ⵏ III	8
Wensleydale	ⵏ ⵏ ⵏ ⵏ IIII	24

Page 10 — Bar Chart

"Broughton Canoe Club...."
21 - 30 was the most common group of marks.
15 + 25 + 30 + 20 = 90 rats entered the
competition.
40 got fewer than half marks.

"Sheep going baa..."
There were **71 sheep**. **Yes** — more than half went baa.

Page 11 — Pie Charts

"Truffle hunting..."
½ went to Grizedale Forest, ⅜ went to Kirby Moor.

⅓ stayed on a campsite, **17 %** stayed in a luxury hotel,

Answers: Pages 11-20

50% went to a bed and breakfast,
24 × 17% = **4** pigs stayed in a luxury hotel,
24 × 50% = **12** stayed on a campsite.

Page 12 — Mental Calculation Strategies

"Three other things...."

5.98 + 2.53 = **8.51** so	1005 – 454 = **551** so
8.51 – 2.53 = 5.98	**454 + 551 = 1005**
8.51 – 5.98 = 2.53	**551 + 454 = 1005**
2.53 + 5.98 = 8.51	**1005 – 551 = 454**

"Use the sum in the example..."
7065 + 1360 = **8425**, 8420 – 7070 = **1350**,
8420 – 1356 = **7064** 1356 + 7062 = **8418**,

"Laura collects..."
1170 – 692 = **478**   1169 – 475 = **694**
690 + 477 = **1167**   480 + 692 = **1172**

Page 13 — Mental Calculation Strategies

"Sums in your head..."
200, 170, 190, 250, 300

"Finding pairs that add up...":
(53 + 37) + 12 = 90 + 12 = **102**   (38 + 12) + 56 = 50 + 56 = **115**
18 + (31 + 29) = 18 + 60 = 78   **55** + (26 + 14) = 55 + 40 = 95
49 + (28 + 42) = 49 + 70 = **119**   (72 + 18) + 79 = 90 + 79 = **169**
38 + (15 + 35) = 38 + 50 = 88   **20** + (16 + 64) = 20 + 80 = 100

"Starting with the biggest..."
70 + 15 + 14 = 85 + 14 = **99**
21 + 88 + 12 = 109 + 12 = **121**
19 + 14 + 92 = 111 + 14 = **125**

Page 14 — Mental Calculation Strategies

"The easy way..."
263 : **five lots of 50 is 250, 3 + 5 + 0 + 4 + 1 = 13,**
    250 + 13 = 263
272: three lots of 90 is 270, 0 + 3 − 1 = 2 and
270 + 2 = 272
284: four lots of 70 is 280, 3 + 0 − 3 + 4 is 4 and
280 + 4 = 284
210: five lots of 40 is 200, 0 + 2 + 1 + 4 + 3 = 10,
    200 + 10 = 210
329: four lots of 80 is 320, −1 + 3 + 2 + 5 is 9
320 + 9 = 329

Page 15 — Mental Calculation Strategies

"Three rules to answer these questions..."
47 + 38 = 85, with the 00s is **8500**
73 – 27 = 46, with the 00s is **4600**
23 + 49 = 72, with the 00s is **7200**
76 – 39 = 37, with the 00s is **3700**

"Use the same method..."
3200 + **1900** = 5100   **3700** + 5200 = 8900
11200 – 8400 = 2800   10100 – **4100** = 6000
9700 + **2800** = 12500   **7100** – 4600 = 2500

Page 16 — Column Addition

"Use carrying to add up..."

5743	4975	8642	4534
+ 7869	+ 2645	+ 5979	+ 5724
13612	**7620**	**14621**	**10258**
1 1 1	1 1 1	1 1 1	1

21	424	26991	5283
14596	5586	33492	87
6	564	2	45533
7532	97	12	9602
+ 977	+ 5312	+ 864	+ 790
23132	**11983**	**61361**	**61295**
1 2 2 2	1 2 2	1 2 2 1	2 2 2 1

Page 17 — Column Subtraction

"Use borrowing..."

5 11 15	5 11 13	8 13 12	5 14 11	8 13 12	1 1 5	5 10 11 13
7625	6123	9427	784651	209427	527625	46123
−3098	−2204	−2882	− 1573	− 4867	− 6108	− 4248
4527	**3919**	**6545**	**783078**	**204560**	**521517**	**41875**

Page 18 — Addition and Subtraction Problems

"Bewildered versus The Borrs..."
6269 – 3585 = 2684 people preferred Bewildered.

"Super Pointing Finger Man..."
Made 7352 + 3947 + 14742 = **26041** points
altogether.
Fred made 7352 – 3947 = **3405** points more than
Rolf.
Jerry made 14 742 – (7352 + 3947) = **3443** points
more.

Page 19 — Checking Results

"Do these sums yourself..."
49 023   **566 458**
Derek grew £3792 + £5874 + £10 923 = **£20 589** on
his trees.   Calculator display: **20589**
He has £20 589 – £1786 = **£18 803** left.
Calculator display: **18803**

Page 20 — Odd and Even Numbers

"Product of three odd numbers is odd": **True**, for
example
3 × 3 × 1 = 9   **3 × 7 × 5 = 105**
7 × 9 × 7 = 441

*"Two even numbers multiplied together give an odd
number"*:
False, for example   **2 × 2 = 4**   **14 × 8 = 112**
10 × 4 = 40

Answers: Pages 20–27

"Complete these statements"
Multiply any two even numbers...always get an **even** number
Product of an **odd** number and an **even** number is always odd.
The product of two even numbers and an odd number is **odd**.

"Write the numbers below as twice a number plus one":
21 is twice 10 plus 1   17 is **twice 8 plus 1**
49 is **twice 24 plus 1**   101 is **twice 50 plus 1**
67 is **twice 33 plus 1**   83 is **twice 41 plus 1**

Page 21 — Properties of Numbers

"...divisible by three": 213, **513**, **1527**, **3336**

"...multiples of eight": 5592 **1888**, **4608**, **9536**

"...have 9 as a factor": 3249, **9855**, **1818**, **9495**, **8584**

"...are multiples of 6": **426**, **126**, **3528**

Page 22 — Properties of Numbers

"Beanthwaite Safari Park..."
The 62nd elephant is **Blue**. The 109th elephant is **Brown.**
The 17th blue elephant is **42nd**.

"Use multiples to answer..."
24, **30**, **24**

Page 23 — Properties of Numbers

"Fill in the gaps for these square numbers..."
$1^2 = 1$ $4^2 = \mathbf{16}$ $7^2 = 49$ $10^2 = \mathbf{100}$
$2^2 = 4$ $5^2 = 25$ $8^2 = \mathbf{64}$ $11^2 = 121$
$3^2 = \mathbf{9}$ $6^2 = \mathbf{36}$ $9^2 = 81$ $12^2 = \mathbf{144}$

"Work out these square numbers..."
$15^2 = 15 \times 15 = \mathbf{225}$ $18^2 = \mathbf{18 \times 18} = \mathbf{324}$
$21^2 = 21 \times 21 = \mathbf{441}$ $30^2 = \mathbf{30 \times 30} = \mathbf{900}$

"Calculator questions..."
$53 \times 53 = 2809$ $\mathbf{66 \times 66} = 4356$ $\mathbf{89 \times 89} = 7921$
$\mathbf{58 \times 58} = 3364$ $\mathbf{74 \times 74} = 5476$
The length of the sides are **16 cm** for the 256 cm² square and **23 cm** for the 529 cm².

Page 24 — Reasoning about Numbers

"You'll need a calculator and guesswork...":
product of 9506: **97 × 98**
product of 3080: **55 × 56**
Fill in the gaps: **647 × 32** = 20704

"Here's one to get you thinking...":
599, **689**, **779**, **869**, **959**, **698**,
797, **896**, **995**, **788**, **878**, **887**,
995, **986**, **977**, **968**
That's **16** in total.

×	2	4	7	8
3	6	12	21	24
5	10	20	35	40
6	12	24	42	48
9	18	36	63	72

"My secret code": A = **1**, B = **8**, C = **6**, D = **4**,
E = **2**, F = **0**, G = **3**

Page 25 — Reasoning about Numbers

"A brain teaser.."
$3 \times 54 = 162$

"Make a formula to work out numbers in a number sequence":
4 balls, 7 balls, **10** balls.
$4 = 1 + 3$, $7 = 1 + 6$ $\mathbf{10 = 1 + 9}$
Number of balls in a pattern $N = 1 + \mathbf{3 \times N}$.
In pattern 8 there are **25** balls,
in pattern 15 there are **46** balls

"Here's a square":

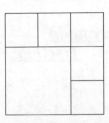

"This is half of a shape...":
Any reasonable answers,
for example:

Page 26 — Place Value, Order and Rounding

"Put these integers in order.."
−48, −7, −2, 2, 26   **−14, −13, −4, 12, 45**   **−37, −35, −33, 31, 39**

"Make a list of pairs of numbers that add up to 17":
Any correct answers. Examples are:
10 and 7, **9 and 8**, **6 and 11**, **5 and 12**, **4 and 13**, **3 and 14**, **2 and 15**, **1 and 16**, **−1 and 18**, **−100 and 117**, **−10 and 27**

Page 27 — Place Value, Order and Rounding

"Answer these temperature questions..."
−10°C,   **6°C**,   **−11°C**,   **15°C**,   **20°C**

Answers: Pages 27–36

"Derek's holiday in Iceland.."

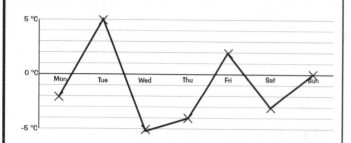

Page 28 — Division — Answering in Fractions

"Write the quotient as a fraction..."

$27 \div 5 = 5\frac{2}{5}$ $50 \div 9 = 5\frac{5}{9}$ $42 \div 4 = 10\frac{1}{2}$

$40 \div 7 = 5\frac{5}{7}$ $43 \div 7 = 6\frac{1}{7}$ $52 \div 6 = 8\frac{2}{3}$

$90 \div 8 = 11\frac{1}{4}$ $52 \div 4 = 13$ $75 \div 10 = 7\frac{1}{2}$

$45 \div 4 = 11\frac{1}{4}$ $45 \div 4 = 11\frac{1}{4}$ $23 \div 3 = 7\frac{2}{3}$

$111 \div 10 = 11\frac{1}{10}$ $89 \div 9 = 9\frac{8}{9}$ $72 \div 5 = 14\frac{2}{5}$

$34 \div 3 = 11\frac{1}{3}$ $65 \div 6 = 10\frac{5}{6}$ $47 \div 6 = 7\frac{5}{6}$

"In one of my dreams...": $9\frac{2}{5}$

Page 29 — Division — Answering in Fractions

"You should be able to do these in your head..."

$50 \div 4 = \underline{12.5}$ $13 \div 2 = \underline{6.5}$ $15 \div 2 = \underline{7.5}$

$98 \div 10 = \underline{9.8}$ $46 \div 10 = \underline{4.6}$ $33 \div 4 = \underline{8.25}$

$45 \div 4 = \underline{11.25}$ $535 \div 100 = \underline{5.35}$ $77 \div 10 = \underline{7.7}$

"These are a bit trickier, so use a calculator..."

$674 \div 8 = \underline{84.25}$ $169 \div 9 = \underline{18.8}$

$196 \div 5 = \underline{39.2}$

$498 \div 4 = \underline{124.5}$ $851 \div 12 = \underline{70.9}$

$358 \div 8 = \underline{44.75}$ $642 \div 9 = \underline{71.3}$

$412 \div 5 = \underline{82.4}$ $724 \div 8 = \underline{90.5}$

Page 30 — Division — Rounding Answers

Wombat Airlines need **7 planes**.

They need **13 boxes** to feed 184 passengers.

5 boxes can be completely filled.

Wombat Airlines can land **3 planes** with £3542.

Dorothy can land **15 houses**.

Page 31 — Quick Ways for Calculations

"Practise these questions..."

$49 \times 7 = \underline{40 \times 7 + 9 \times 7 = 280 + 63 = 343}$

$56 \times 4 = \underline{50 \times 4 + 6 \times 4 = 200 + 24 = 224}$

$88 \times 8 = \underline{80 \times 8 + 8 \times 8 = 640 + 64 = 704}$

"Split these numbers into units and tenths..."

$7.4 \times 6 = \underline{7 \times 6 + 0.4 \times 6 = 42 + 2.4 = 44.4}$

$9.3 \times 5 = \underline{9 \times 5 + 0.3 \times 5 = 45 + 1.5 = 46.5}$

$3.1 \times 7 = \underline{3 \times 7 + 0.1 \times 7 = 21 + 0.7 = 21.7}$

$8.7 \times 9 = \underline{8 \times 9 + 0.7 \times 9 = 72 + 6.3 + 78.3}$

$5.6 \times 8 = \underline{5 \times 8 + 0.6 \times 8 = 40 + 4.8 = 44.8}$

"Maurice Moose really impressed..." He scored **88.2**.

Page 32 — Fractions as Division

"Fractions of these questions..."

12, **7**, **25**, **7**

"Silly Football question..."

20, **50**, **30**, **70**

$580 \times 0.5 = \underline{290}$ $420 \times 0.75 = \underline{315}$ $760 \times 0.25 = \underline{190}$

Page 33 — Doing Decimals in Your Head

double $3.5 = \underline{7}$ double $1.7 = \underline{3.4}$

double $4.3 = \underline{8.6}$ half $6.42 = \underline{3.21}$

$0.5 \times 7 = \underline{3.5}$ $0.6 \times 8 = \underline{4.8}$ $0.4 \times 5 = \underline{2}$ $1.4 \times 10 = \underline{14}$

$3.65 \times 10 = \underline{36.5}$ $3.65 \times 100 = \underline{365}$ $1.9 \times 100 = \underline{190}$

$0.7 \times 10 = \underline{70}$ $0.08 \times 10 = \underline{0.8}$

Page 34 — Written Methods for Multiplication

"Approximate the answer first..."

279×11 is about $\underline{280 \times 10 = 2800}$

457×92 is about $\underline{460 \times 90 = 41\,400}$

634×83 is about $\underline{630 \times 80 = 50\,400}$

"Multiply each digit separately..."

$279 \times 11 = \underline{(2000 + 700 + 90) + (200 + 70 + 9) = 3069}$

$634 \times 83 = \underline{(48\,000 + 2400 + 320) + (1800 + 90 + 12) = 52\,622}$

$457 \times 92 = \underline{(36\,000 + 4500 + 630) + (800 + 100 + 14) = 42\,044}$

Page 35 — Written Methods for Division

"Find approximate answers..."

$396 \div 11$ is about $\underline{400 \div 10 = 40}$

$504 \div 19$ is about $\underline{500 \div 20 = 25}$

$928 \div 27$ is about $\underline{930 \div 30 = 31}$

"Exact answers to these divisions..."

$396 \div 11 = \underline{36}$ $504 \div 19 =$ **26 r 10** $928 \div 27 =$ **34 r10**

$396 - 330 = 66$ $504 - 380 = 124$ $928 - 810 = 118$

$66 - 55 = 11$ $124 - 95 = 29$ $118 - 54 = 64$

$11 - 11 = 0$ $29 - 19 = 10$ $64 - 54 = 10$

$\underline{30 + 5 + 1 = 36}$ $\underline{20 + 5 + 1 = 26}$ $\underline{30 + 2 + 2 = 34}$

remainder 10   **remainder 10**

Page 36 — Real Life Problems

"Wacky Tea Bag Collection..." Cost £1.35 × 3 = **£4.05** in total.

"Wacky Tea Bag Ride..." Costs £3.60 ÷ 6 = **60 p** per go.

"Sheep counting contest..." They count 173 × 3 = **519** sheep.

"1038 sheep in total..." The concert lasts 1038 ÷ 519 = **2 hours**.

"Flossybot Parsons..." Appears 37 × 8 = **296** times.

Page 37 — Real Life Problems

"While passing Saturn..." Noel takes 16 × 35 = **560** photos.

"They stop off at Jupiter..." Each friend gets 232 ÷ 14 = **16** photos, with 232 − 224 = **8** photos left over.

"Joel's planet..."

Think of 167 ÷ 15 = **11$\frac{2}{15}$** names per person.

"Paul's yellow aliens.."
He gives them 12 × 0.75 = **£9** in total.

Page 38 — Function Machines

"One number goes in..."
56 ÷ 8 = **7** 1.5 × 100 = **150**
7 + 13 = **20**
70 − 25 = **45** 12 + 15 = **27**
6 × 12 = **72** 32 × 3 = **96** 84 ÷ 7 = **12**

Page 39 — Function Machines

"What number went into the machine..."
100 ÷ 2 = **50**
78 ÷ 6 = **13** 130 + 50 = **180**

"What's between..."
23.7 ÷ **10** = 2.37 12 × **12** = 144
185 − **150** = 35 38 ÷ **100** = 0.38
260 ÷ **26** = 10

Page 40 — Real Life Problems — Calculators

"Paul, Noel and Joel..." Find 19 × 31 = **589** fish in total.
"Joel sees..." 160 ÷ 32 = **5** kinds of seagull.
"UFO beams up..." 12 × 5 = **60** seagulls.
"Which leaves..." 160 − 60 = **100** seagulls.
"Mountain climbing.." They climb 208 ÷ 52 = **4** mountains a week.

Page 41 — What are Percentages?

"Write as a percentage.."
$\frac{75}{100}$ = **75%** $\frac{59}{100}$ = **59%** $\frac{10}{100}$ = **10%** 87% = $\frac{87}{100}$
"Write as a decimal.."
75% = $\frac{3}{4}$ = **0.75** 30% = $\frac{3}{10}$ = **0.3**

Page 42 — Percentages, Decimals & Fractions

"Change a percentage into..."
60% = $\frac{3}{5}$ 80% = $\frac{4}{5}$ 16% = **0.16** 5% = **0.05**

0.24 = **24%** $\frac{4}{5}$ = **80%**

Page 43 — Finding Percentages

"Find 25%..." **quarter it**.

"Honey-Nut Sproutflakes..." Half of 500 g = **250 g**.
Get 500 g + 250 g = **750 g**.

"50% of these amounts..."
£36 × 50% = **£18** 200m × 50% = **100 m** 60 miles × 50% = **30 miles**
"Vic chops cheese.." 160 tonnes ÷ 4 = **40 tonnes**.
"Moth eaten dresses..." £12.80 × 25% = **£3.20 knocked off**.
"Ace Moldo Sweets.." 20 × 25% = **5 extra sweets**.
20 + 5 = **25 sweets in total**.

Page 44 — Finding Percentages

"Silecroft Kite-Flying Tournament.."
38 ÷ 100 × 200 = **76 seagulls**.
"Percentages.."
14% × 550 = 77 ferret enthusiasts.
90% of 1000 = 900 lemon drinks.

"Bewildered's Intelligence Test.."
Linseed: **870** Sinbad: **2460** Kevin: **3000**
O'Dear: **2310**

"Pet Dragons..."
72% don't eat fish, which is **36 dragons** altogether.

"Soggy peas..."
25% × 64 = **16 peas hit Jon**.

"Witches..."
20 × 90% = 18 are witches.
20 − 18 = **2 aren't witches**.

Page 45 — Percentages

"Mouse has increased..."
in value to 30% × £23 000 = £6900
£23 000 + £6900 = **£29 900**

"Interest.."
5% × £75 = **£3.75** interest.
Have £3.75 + £75 = **£78.75** now.

"Kirby United replica shirt.."
20% × £30 = £6. It costs £30 − £6 = **£24**

"Pensioners pay..."
60% × £20 = £12, £20 − £12 = **£8**

Page 46 — Percentages

"Jasper's tax..." £1080 × 33% = **£356.40**
"Jasper puts..." £320 × 12% = **£38.40**

"Round to the nearest whole number..."
(38 ÷ 42) × 100 = **90%**
(42 ÷ 70) × 100 = **60%**
(149 ÷ 219) × 100 = **68%**

Page 47 — Mode and Range

"Give the mode.." **15** **7**
103 **10**

"Alien's heights..." **3-4 metres**.

"Give the range..." **34** **77**
196 **60**

Answers: Pages 48–53

Page 48 — Finding Averages

"Put the numbers in order..."
9, 9, 10, 11, 12, 12, 13, 13, 14, 15
...the middle comes between the fifth and the **sixth** score.
The fifth and sixth scores are both **12**. So the median
score is **12**.

"Average..."
9 + 9 + 10 + 11 + 12 + 12 + 13 + 13 + 14
+ 15 = **118**, **118** ÷ 10 = **11.8**. The mean score is **11.8**

Page 49 — Finding Averages

"Chocolate cookie pizza..."
17, 18, 20, 22, 23, 26, 35. Median = **22 pizzas**,
Total = **161 pizzas**, mean = **161 ÷ 7 = 23 pizzas**

"Millom Mud Museum.."
45, 50, 55, 60, 75, 90, 90, 100, 135, 145, 170, 185.
Median = **90 visitors** , total = **1200 visitors**, divide by **12**
to find the mean, **1200 ÷ 12 = 100 visitors**.

Page 50 — Line Graphs

"Islanders of Noonos...."

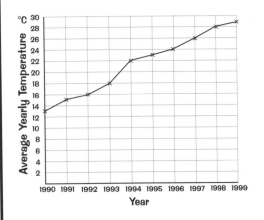

"Use the time graph..."

1990	145 mm		1995	90 mm
1991	130 mm		1996	95 mm
1992	125 mm		1997	75 mm
1993	105 mm		1998	50 mm
1994	115 mm		1999	55 mm

Page 51 — Line Graphs

"Km-miles line graph..."
40 km to Trunkton
23 km = **14 miles**, 44 miles = **70 km**, 57 km = **36
miles**
17 miles = **26 km**

"Exchange rate..."

£2.40 = **35 schmollars**, 94 schmollars = **£6.75**,
£8.75 = **123 schmollars**, 136 schmollars = **£9.75**

Page 52 — Rotation

"Rotate 90° clockwise around X..."

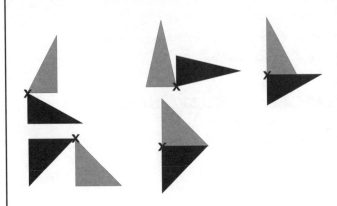

Page 53 — Rotation

"Rotate through 180°..."

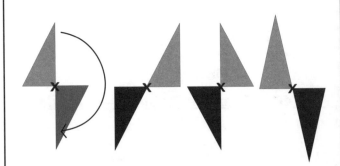

"Rotate these shapes and give coordinates.."

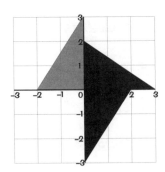

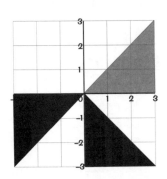

Answers: Pages 53–66

rotated 90° - **(0,0) (3,0) (0,2)** rotated 90° **(0,0) (0,–3)**
(3,–3)

new shape - **(0,0) (0,–3) (2,0)** new shape **(0,0) (–3,0)**
(–3,–3)

Page 54 — Angles

"Right word under each angle.."
acute, **obtuse**, **acute**, **acute**,
obtuse, **obtuse**.

"Order of smallest to biggest..."
A is about 45°, B is about **70°**, C is about **130°**,
D is about **105°**, E is about **30°**, F is about **165°**.
in order of size: **E, A, B, D, C, F**.
Angles **A, B & E** are acute, angles **C, D & F** are obtuse

Page 55 — Angles

"Use a protractor..."

115° obtuse	**45° acute**
56° acute	**157° obtuse**
35° acute	**30° acute**.

For drawings, accept angles within 1°.

Page 56 — Angles of a Triangle

Measure angles in these triangles.."
Left hand triangle: A = **65°** B = **62°** C = **53°**
add up to **180°**
Right hand triangle: A = **35°** B = **120°** C = **25°**
add up to **180°**

Page 57 — Angles of a Triangle

"Missing angles of a triangle..."
180° – 73° – 33° = **74°** 180° – 60° – 49° = **71°**
180° – 59° – 34° = **87°** 180° – 29° – **90°** = **61°**

"Isosceles...."
180° – (38° + **38°**) = **104°**
180° – 126° = 54°, 54° ÷ 2 = **27° & 27°**

Page 58 — Reflex Angles

"Write under each angle..."
acute, **reflex**, **obtuse**, **reflex**

For drawings, check the angles are greater than 180°.

Page 59 — Angles at a Point

"Find the missing angles..."
360° – 110° = **250°**   360° – 65° = **295°**
360° – 60° = **300°**   360° – 108° = **252°**
360° – 90° = **270°**

Page 60 — Reasoning About Shapes

"The Martian's statement..."
All angles of the quadrilateral I've drawn are **90°**.
But the Martian is **wrong**. The King is **wrong** as well.

Page 61 — Reasoning About Shapes

"Test the statement.."
108° × 5 = **540°**   120° × 6 = **720°**
135° × 8 = **1080°**
So all of the drawn shapes have angles adding up to more
than 360°. In fact it's **true** in general.

Page 62 — Units of Time

"Time sums..."
1030 years, **214** seconds, **1347** years.

"Days in each month..."
September = **30** days, October = **31** days,
March = **31** days, April **30** days and May = **31** days,
February in a leap year **29** days,
every other year = **28** days.

Page 63 — Problems Involving Time

"Nut roast..."
A 3kg roast takes **2 hours & 15 minutes**
A 5 kg roast takes **3 hours & 45 minutes**.

"Albert decides to buy a huge new cooker..."
Still paying in 2 years time: **yes**, in 3 years: **no**.
Covered by the guarantee: **yes**, after 23 years: **no**.

"Albert employs Derek..."
Washes up **50 plates** in 10 mins.
Takes **25 minutes** for 125 plates.
It's **May**. Derek gets his bonus in **8** days.

Page 64 — Time Zones

"Time questions..."
At 1 pm in Britain: It's **11 pm** in Brisbane and
8 am in NY.
At 8:45 pm in Britain: It's **6:45 pm** in Brisbane and
3:45 am in NY.

Page 65 — Time Zones

"Look at the map..."
Stacey's clock says **8:30 pm**. The clocks in Carrot City say **9:15am**.
Turn the TV on at **4:30 pm** in Spinachston. Have to wait **2 hours**.
"British Summer Time..."
It'll get dark at **5 pm** tomorrow, it'll get light at **6 am**
tomorrow and it'll be **8 am** 12 hours.

Page 66 — Mental Calculation

"Bob's weightlifting bar..."
He has to add 7 – 6.53 kg = **0.47** kg to round it up.

"Jelly-Flop Finals..."
She needs 55 – 54.32 = **0.68** points.

"Quick sums..."
3.72 + **0.28** = 4   2.44 + **0.56** = 3   6.79 + **0.21** = 7
0.01 + 9.99 = 10   **0.35** + 0.65 = 1   **0.68** + 4.32 = 5

Answers: Pages 67–74

Page 67 — Mental Calculations

"Add up the tenths.." **0.3** *"Add up the hundredths..."* **0.09**, *"So they have raised..."*: **0.39 p**

Mary has **0.43 kg** of custard powder.

$0.63 + 0.04 = $ **0.67** $0.66 - 0.12 = $ **0.54** $0.37 - 0.26 = $ **0.11**
$0.49 + 0.3 = $ **0.79** $0.44 - 0.2 = $ **0.24** $0.9 + 0.01 = $ **0.91**
$0.68 + 0.11 = $ **0.79** $0.19 - 0.11 = $ **0.08** $0.98 - 0.36 = $ **0.62**

Page 68 — Adding Decimals

"Have a go at these.."
839.17, **1967.27**

"Have a go at these.."
1377.23, **532.69**, **3257.02**, **1634.46**

"Lincoln's Largest Lemon competition..."
The lemon is **1.6 kg**.

Page 69 — Subtracting Decimals

"Practice for you..."
726.91, **1346.57**

"No columns..."
492.57, **330.42**, **1468.**1, **7251.94**.

"Lincoln's Largest Lemon competition..."
The weight of the chunk the grub ate is **1.7 kg**.

Page 70 — Prime Numbers

"Work out if these are primes":
40: $40 \div 2 = 20$ *or* 40 ends in an even number, so **40 isn't a prime**.
41: $41 \div 2 = 20$ rem 1, $41 \div 3 = 13$ rem 2, $41 \div 5 = 8$ rem 1, $41 \div 7 = 5$ rem 6, $41 \div 11 = 3$ rem 8, $41 \div 13 = 3$ rem 2, $41 \div 17 = 2$ rem 7, $41 \div 19 = 2$ rem 3, and 23 is over half 41, so **41 is prime**.

"Some more quick ones...": **13**, **2**, **17**, **29** are primes.

Page 71 — Factors and Dividing

"Write down the factors..."
20: **1, 2, 4, 5, 10, 20**   15: **1, 3, 5, 15**
36: **1, 2, 3, 4, 6, 9, 12, 18, 36**   80: **1, 2, 4, 5, 8, 10, 16, 20, 40, 80**

"...into prime factors..."
60: **2, 2, 3, 5** 84: **2, 2, 3, 7** 92: **2, 2, 23**

Page 72 — Using Formulas to Solve Problems

"Use the formula to solve these problems.."
49 500p or £495,   **198p or £1.98**,   **23 562p or £235.62**

Total cost of sweets: **c = 55 × n**. It costs him $55 \times 6 = $ **330p or £3.30**

Page 73 — Using Formulas to Solve Problems

"Farmer Fields.."   **p = f + 1**,
                21 posts.
                P = 2L + 2W

"Now use your formula..." **121** posts
                50 m

Page 74 — Investigating General Statements

Any sensible examples. For example:
$$2 \times 25 = 50 = 2 \times 100 \div 4$$

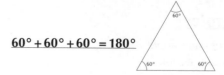

$$60° + 60° + 60° = 180°$$

$12 \div 6 = 2$ and 12 is even, $4 \times 3 = 12$ and $3 \times 4 = 12$

Index

Numbers and Stuff
cm² 4, 5
% 41, 42, 43, 44, 45

A
acute angles 54, 55, 58
adding decimals 66, 67, 68
adding in columns 68
addition 12, 14, 16, 18
angles 54, 55, 56, 57, 58, 59, 60
angle statements 60, 61
approximating sums 34, 35
area 4, 5
average 48, 50

B
bar charts 8, 10
Billy Bonker 72
borrowing numbers 17, 18
brain-teasers 24, 25
British Summer Time 65

C
calculators 19, 29, 32, 40, 46
carrying numbers 16, 18
centuries 62
charts 8, 9, 10
checking answers 19, 40
Chimps Incorporated 46
clockwise 52
centimetres (cm) 2, 3, 4, 5, 6
column sums 16, 17
consecutive numbers 74
converting fractions 41, 42
converting measurements 7, 51

coordinates 53
corners 52

D
data sets 48, 49
days 62
decades 62
decimal point 67, 68, 69
decimals 29, 33, 41, 42, 66, 67, 68
divisibility 21
division 28, 29, 30, 32, 35, 71
division and shapes 5
division for percentages 46
doubling 33, 39
drawing 50, 55

E
estimating measurements 7
even numbers 20
exchange rate 51
explaining sums 15

F
factors 21, 22, 71
feet 6
flying hippos 28
formulas 72, 73
fractions 11, 32, 41, 42, 44
frequency tables 9
function machines 38, 39
Furness Towers 36

G
gallons 1, 6
general statements 74
grams (g) 1, 6
graphs 8, 9, 10, 50, 51
Greenwich Mean Time 65

H
half 32
half turn 52, 58, 59
halving 38, 43
Honey-Nut Sproutflakes 43
hundreds 16, 17, 34
hundredths 67

I
imperial units 1, 7
improper fractions 28
inches (in) 6
inner angles 60
integers 26
interest 45
investigating statements 60, 61, 74
isosceles triangle 57

J
jelly-flop finals 67

K
kilograms (kg) 6, 63
kilometres (km) 1, 6, 51, 68

L
length 3, 4, 5, 7, 73
letters as numbers 72
Lincoln's largest lemon 68
line graphs 50, 51
litres (l) 1, 6

M
mean 48, 49
measurements 6, 7, 55
measuring units 1, 6, 7
median 48, 49
mental calculations 12, 13, 14, 15, 33, 66, 67
metres (m) 1, 4, 5, 6

Index

metric units 1, 6, 7
miles 1, 51
millennium 62
millilitres (ml) 6, 7
millimetres (mm) 50
minutes 62, 63
mode 47, 48
mole-vaulting competition
    67
money 18, 45
months 62, 63
multiples 12, 21, 22, 35
multiplication 23, 28,
    30, 34, 35
multiplying decimals 33

N
negative numbers 26, 27
number puzzles 24

O
obtuse 54, 58
odd numbers 20
Orang-u-Corp 46
ordering negative numbers
    26
ounces (oz) 1, 6
Outer Space Tours 36

P
pairs of numbers 26
patterns 25
percentages 41, 42, 43,
    44, 45, 46
perimeters 2, 3, 73
pictogram 9
pie charts 11
pints (pt) 1
place value 26
pounds (lb) 1, 6, 7
prime factors 70

prime numbers 70
problems involving time 63
problems with formulas 72
properties of numbers
    20, 21
proportion 46
protractor 55, 56

Q
quadrilateral 60
quarter turn 52, 58, 59
quartering 43
quotient 28, 29

R
range 47, 48
real life problems 36, 37,
    40
reasoning about numbers
    24, 25
reasoning about shapes
    60, 61
rectangles 4, 5, 73
reflex angles 58
remainders 21, 22, 28, 70
right-angled triangle 5
rotation 52, 53
rounding numbers
    30, 34, 46

S
seconds 62, 63
shapes 52, 60, 61
Sludge's Sweets 72
smallest common multiple
    22
soggy peas 44
square 25
square numbers 23
statement on angles 61
statements about sums 74

Stella Burgers 47
straight angle 56
subtracting decimals
    67, 69
subtracting in columns 68
subtraction 12, 17, 18

T
tables 8, 9, 50
tally charts 8, 9
temperature 27
tens 16, 17, 34
tenths 67
thousands 16, 17
time 62, 63, 64, 65
time zones 64
times table 22, 24
triangle 56, 57
truffle-hunting 11

U
UFO's 40
Ulverston Unicycle
    Academy 46
units 6, 16, 17, 34, 62

V
vermin pie 7

W
wacky tea bags 37
weeks 62
weight 7
width 4, 5, 73
written methods 34, 35

Y
years 62

Z
zero 13, 26